Boston

Official Bartender's Guide

Compiled and Edited by Leo Cotton

PUBLISHED BY
MR. BOSTON DISTILLER INC. BOSTON, MASSACHUSETTS

Mr. Boston Bartender Guide

1st printing January 1935
2nd printing March 1935
3rd printing October 1936
4th printing (revised) September 1940
5th printing October 1941
6th printing November 1946
7th printing December 1948
8th printing September 1949
9th printing February 1951
10th printing April 1953
11th printing December 1953
12th printing (revised) July 1955
13th printing September 1957
14th printing May 1959
15th printing December 1959
16th printing (revised) August 1960
17th printing January 1961
18th printing June 1961
19th printing September 1961
20th printing October 1961
21st printing December 1962
22nd printing January 1963

23rd printing August 1963
24th printing October 1963
25th printing November 1963
26th printing December 1963
27th printing May 1964
28th printing November 1964
29th printing January 1965
30th printing April 1965
31st printing May 1965
32nd printing October 1965
33rd printing November 1965
34th printing January 1966
35th printing February 1966
36th printing August 1966
37th printing January 1967
38th printing February 1967
39th printing May 1967
40th printing September 1967
41st printing January 1968
42nd printing April 1968
43rd printing May 1968
44th printing November 1968

LIBRARY OF CONGRESS CATALOG NUMBER: 60-15939

Printed in U.S.A.

Acknowledgements

APPRECIATION IS ACKNOWLEDGED to Joseph DeSoto, founder and chief instructor of the original Boston Bartender's School and to the many other bartenders who contributed their assistance.

EDITOR

Contents

An Introduction to the Art of Good Mixing and Good Living

THE FIRST edition of the OLD MR. BOSTON OFFICIAL BAR-
TENDER'S GUIDE was published in 1935 to provide an authentic
and accurate recipe book. It was dedicated to the thousands of
bartenders throughout the country and to all others who felt
the need for an official source of information for mixing drinks.

Since that date more than four million copies have been
sold and to commemorate the Silver Anniversary edition issued
in 1960 it was completely revised from cover to cover. Handsome new color pages were included with an easier to read
format. Special sections on Eggnogs, The Martini, Bar Hints and
Measurements were added together with a Liquor Dictionary and
many new recipes. The demand has been so great that this reprint
is now necessary and as it is the desire of the editor to constantly
keep this book up to date, additional revisions and drinks which
have become popular, even in the short time since the last edition, are now included. It is gratifying to learn from the innumer-
able letters which have been received that this book is considered
one of the finest and most authentic drink-recipe books ever
published.

Old Mr. Boston will appear frequently throughout the pages
of this book. He is a rare and versatile gentleman, everlastingly
young and ever ready to accept the difficult role of host. Follow the advice of this joyful and genial friend and there will be
many pleasant times in store for you. We know you are going
to like Old Mr. Boston.

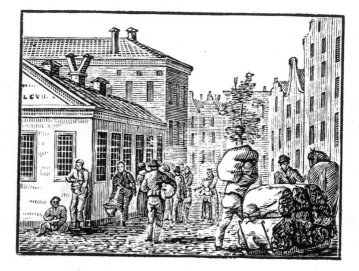

A

ABBEY COCKTAIL

1½ oz. Old Mr. Boston Dry Gin
Juice of ¼ Orange
1 Dash Orange Bitters
Shake well with cracked ice and strain into 3 oz. cocktail glass. Add a Maraschino cherry.

ABSINTHE COCKTAIL

1½ oz. Absinthe Substitute
¾ oz. Water
¼ oz. Old Mr. Boston Anisette
1 Dash Orange Bitters
Shake well with cracked ice and strain into 3 oz. cocktail glass.

ABSINTHE DRIP COCKTAIL

Pour 1½ oz. absinthe substitute into special drip glass or Old Fashioned cocktail glass. Place cube of sugar over hole of drip spoon (or in silver tea strainer). Pack spoon or strainer with cracked ice, pour cold water to fill. When water has dripped through, drink is ready.

ABSINTHE SPECIAL COCKTAIL

1½ oz. Absinthe Substitute
1 oz. Water
¼ Teaspoon Powdered Sugar
1 Dash Orange Bitters
Shake well with cracked ice and strain into 3 oz. cocktail glass.

ADONIS COCKTAIL

1 Dash Orange Bitters
¾ oz. Sweet Vermouth
1½ oz. Dry Sherry Wine
Stir well with cracked ice and strain into 3 oz. cocktail glass.

AFFINITY COCKTAIL

¾ oz. Dry Vermouth
¾ oz. Sweet Vermouth
¾ oz. Old Mr. Boston Scotch Whisky
2 Dashes Orange Bitters
Stir well with cracked ice and strain into 3 oz. cocktail glass.

AFTER DINNER COCKTAIL

1 oz. Old Mr. Boston Apricot Flavored Brandy
1 oz. Curacao
Juice of 1 lime
Shake well with cracked ice and strain into 3 oz. cocktail glass. Leave lime in glass.

A

After Supper Cocktail

1 oz. Old Mr. Boston Apricot
   Flavored Brandy
1 oz. Curacao
½ Teaspoon Lemon Juice
*Shake well with cracked ice and
strain into 3 oz. cocktail glass.*

Alabama Cocktail

½ oz. Lemon Juice
½ Teaspoon Powdered Sugar
1½ oz. Old Mr. Boston Five Star
   Brandy
1 Teaspoon Curacao
*Shake well with cracked ice and
strain into 3 oz. cocktail glass.*

Alabama Fizz

Juice ½ Lemon
1 Teaspoon Powdered Sugar
2 oz. Old Mr. Boston Dry Gin
*Shake well with cracked ice and
strain into 7 oz. highball glass. Fill
with carbonated water. Add 2 sprigs
of fresh mint.*

Alaska Cocktail

2 Dashes Orange Bitters
1½ oz. Old Mr. Boston Dry Gin
¾ oz. Yellow Chartreuse
*Stir well with cracked ice and strain
into 3 oz. cocktail glass.*

Albemarle Fizz

Juice ½ Lemon
1 Teaspoon Powdered Sugar
2 oz. Old Mr. Boston Dry Gin
*Shake well with cracked ice and
strain into 7 oz. highball glass. Fill
with carbonated water. Add 1 teaspoon raspberry syrup.*

Alexander Cocktail No. 1

1 oz. Old Mr. Boston Dry Gin
1 oz. Old Mr. Boston Creme de
   Cacao
1 oz. Sweet Cream
*Shake well with cracked ice and
strain into 4 oz. cocktail glass.*

Alexander Cocktail No. 2

1 oz. Old Mr. Boston Creme de
   Cacao
1 oz. Old Mr. Boston Five Star
   Brandy
1 oz. Sweet Cream
*Shake well with cracked ice and
strain into 4 oz. cocktail glass.*

Alexander's Sister Cocktail

1 oz. Old Mr. Boston Dry Gin
1 oz. Old Mr. Boston Creme de
   Menthe (green)
1 oz. Sweet Cream
*Shake well with cracked ice and
strain into 4 oz. cocktail glass.*

Allen Cocktail

¼ oz. Lemon Juice
¾ oz. Maraschino
1½ oz. Old Mr. Boston Dry Gin
*Shake well with cracked ice and
strain into 3 oz. cocktail glass.*

Allies Cocktail

1 oz. Dry Vermouth
1 oz. Old Mr. Boston Dry Gin
½ Teaspoon Old Mr. Boston
   Kummel
*Stir well with cracked ice and strain
into 3 oz. cocktail glass.*

A

Amer Picon Cocktail

Juice 1 Lime
1 Teaspoon Grenadine
1½ oz. Amer Picon
Shake well with cracked ice and strain into 3 oz. cocktail glass.

American Beauty Cocktail

½ oz. Orange Juice
½ oz. Grenadine
½ oz. Dry Vermouth
½ oz. Old Mr. Boston Five Star Brandy
¼ Teaspoon Old Mr. Boston Creme de Menthe (white)
Shake well with cracked ice and strain into 3 oz. cocktail glass and top with a little Port Wine.

American Grog

1 Lump of Sugar
Juice ¼ Lemon
1½ oz. Old Mr. Boston Imported Rum
Fill hot whiskey glass with hot water and stir

Angel's Delight

¼ oz. Grenadine
¼ oz. Triple Sec
¼ oz. Creme de Yvette
¼ oz. Fresh Cream
Pour carefully, in order given, into Pousse Café glass, so that each ingredient floats on preceding one.

Angel's Kiss

¼ oz. Old Mr. Boston Creme de Cacao
¼ oz. Creme de Yvette
¼ oz. Old Mr. Boston Five Star Brandy
¼ oz. Sweet Cream
Pour ingredients carefully, in order given, so that they do not mix. Use Pousse Café glass.

Angel's Tip

¾ oz. Old Mr. Boston Creme de Cacao
¼ oz. Sweet Cream
Float cream and insert toothpick in cherry and put on top. Use Pousse Café glass.

Angel's Wing

⅓ oz. Old Mr. Boston Creme de Cacao
⅓ oz. Old Mr. Boston Five Star Brandy
⅓ oz. Sweet Cream
Pour ingredients carefully, in order given, so that they do not mix. Use Pousse Café glass.

Apple Blow Fizz

White of 1 Egg
Juice ½ Lemon
1 Teaspoon Powdered Sugar
2 oz. Apple Brandy
Shake well with cracked ice and strain into 8 oz. highball glass. Fill with carbonated water.

3

APPLE BRANDY COCKTAIL

1½ oz. Apple Brandy
1 Teaspoon Grenadine
1 Teaspoon Lemon Juice
Shake well with cracked ice and strain into 3 oz. cocktail glass.

APPLE BRANDY HIGHBALL

1 Cube of Ice
2 oz. Apple Brandy
Fill 8 oz. highball glass with ginger ale or carbonated water. Add twist of lemon peel, if desired, and stir.

APPLE BRANDY RICKEY

1 Cube of Ice
Juice of ½ Lime
1½ oz. Apple Brandy
Fill 8 oz. highball glass with carbonated water and stir. Leave lime in glass.

APPLE BRANDY SOUR

Juice ½ Lemon
½ Teaspoon Powdered Sugar
2 oz. Apple Brandy
Shake well with cracked ice and strain into 6 oz. sour glass. Decorate with a half-slice of lemon and a cherry.

APPLE PIE COCKTAIL

¾ oz. Old Mr. Boston Imported Rum
¾ oz. Sweet Vermouth
1 Teaspoon Old Mr. Boston Apricot Flavored Brandy
½ Teaspoon Grenadine
1 Teaspoon Lemon Juice
Shake well with cracked ice and strain into 3 oz. cocktail glass.

APRICOT BRANDY RICKEY

1 Cube of Ice
Juice of ½ Lime
2 oz. Old Mr. Boston Apricot Flavored Brandy
Fill 8 oz. highball glass with carbonated water and stir. Leave lime in glass.

APRICOT COCKTAIL

Juice of ¼ Lemon
Juice of ¼ Orange
1½ oz. Old Mr. Boston Apricot Flavored Brandy
1 Teaspoon Old Mr. Boston Dry Gin
Shake well with cracked ice and strain into 3 oz. cocktail glass.

APRICOT COOLER

Into 12 oz. Tom Collins glass, put:
½ Teaspoon Powdered Sugar
2 oz. Carbonated Water
Stir and fill glass with cracked ice and add:
2 oz. Old Mr. Boston Apricot Flavored Brandy
Fill with carbonated water or ginger ale and stir again. Insert spiral of orange or lemon peel (or both) and dangle end over rim of glass.

APRICOT FIZZ

Juice ½ Lemon
Juice ½ Lime
1 Teaspoon Powdered Sugar
2 oz. Old Mr. Boston Apricot Flavored Brandy
Shake well with cracked ice and strain into 7 oz. highball glass. Fill with carbonated water.

B

B & B

½ oz. Benedictine
½ oz. Cognac
*Use cordial glass and carefully float
the Cognac on top of the Benedictine.*

BABBIE'S SPECIAL COCKTAIL

½ oz. Sweet Cream
1½ oz. Old Mr. Boston Apricot
    Flavored Brandy
¼ Teaspoon Old Mr. Boston Dry
    Gin
*Shake well with cracked ice and
strain into 3 oz. cocktail glass.*

BACARDI COCKTAIL

1½ oz. Bacardi Rum
Juice ½ Lime
½ Teaspoon Grenadine
*Shake well with cracked ice and
strain into 3 oz. cocktail glass.*

BACHELOR'S BAIT COCKTAIL

1½ oz. Old Mr. Boston Dry Gin
White of 1 Egg
1 Dash Orange Bitters
½ Teaspoon Grenadine
*Shake well with cracked ice and
strain into 4 oz. cocktail glass.*

BALTIMORE BRACER COCKTAIL

1 oz. Old Mr. Boston Anisette
1 oz. Old Mr. Boston Five Star
    Brandy
White of 1 Egg
*Shake well with cracked ice and
strain into 4 oz. cocktail glass.*

BALTIMORE EGGNOG

1 Egg
1 Teaspoon Powdered Sugar
1 oz. Old Mr. Boston Five Star
    Brandy
1 oz. Jamaica Rum
1 oz. Madeira Wine
*Fill glass with milk, shake well with
cracked ice and strain into 12 oz.
Tom Collins glass. Grate nutmeg on
top.*

BAMBOO COCKTAIL

1½ oz. Sherry Wine
¾ oz. Dry Vermouth
1 Dash Orange Bitters
*Stir well with cracked ice and strain
into 3 oz. cocktail glass.*

Banana Daiquiri

Same as Frozen Daiquiri Cocktail on page 39, except add 1 sliced medium size ripe banana.

Banana Punch

2 oz. Old Mr. Boston Vodka
¼ oz. Old Mr. Boston Apricot Flavored Brandy
Juice ½ Lime
Pour into 12 oz. Tom Collins glass filled with crushed ice. Add carbonated water and top with sprigs of mint.

Barbary Coast Cocktail

½ oz. Old Mr. Boston Dry Gin
½ oz. Old Mr. Boston Imported Rum
½ oz. Old Mr. Boston Creme de Cacao
½ oz. Old Mr. Boston Scotch Whisky
½ oz. Sweet Cream
Shake well with cracked ice and strain into 4 oz. cocktail glass.

Baron Cocktail

½ oz. Dry Vermouth
1½ oz. Old Mr. Boston Dry Gin
1½ Teaspoons Curacao
½ Teaspoon Sweet Vermouth
Stir well with cracked ice and strain into 3 oz. cocktail glass. Add twist of lemon peel and drop in glass.

Beadlestone Cocktail

1¼ oz. Dry Vermouth
1¼ oz. Old Mr. Boston Scotch Whisky
Stir well with cracked ice and strain into 3 oz. cocktail glass.

Beals Cocktail

1½ oz. Old Mr. Boston Scotch Whisky
½ oz. Dry Vermouth
½ oz. Sweet Vermouth
Stir well with cracked ice and strain into 3 oz. cocktail glass.

Beauty Spot Cocktail

1 Teaspoon Orange Juice
½ oz. Sweet Vermouth
½ oz. Dry Vermouth
1 oz. Old Mr. Boston Dry Gin
Shake well with cracked ice and strain into 3 oz. cocktail glass, with a dash of grenadine in bottom of glass.

Belmont Cocktail

2 oz. Old Mr. Boston Dry Gin
1 Teaspoon Raspberry Syrup
¾ oz. Sweet Cream
Shake well with cracked ice and strain into 4 oz. cocktail glass.

Bennett Cocktail

Juice of ½ Lime
1½ oz. Old Mr. Boston Dry Gin
½ Teaspoon Powdered Sugar
2 Dashes Orange Bitters
Shake well with cracked ice and strain into 3 oz. cocktail glass.

B

BERMUDA BOUQUET

Juice ¼ Orange
Juice ½ Lemon
1 Teaspoon Powdered Sugar
1½ oz. Old Mr. Boston Dry Gin
1 oz. Old Mr. Boston Apricot
  Flavored Brandy
1 Teaspoon Grenadine
½ Teaspoon Curacao
*Shake well with cracked ice and
strain into 8 oz. highball glass.*

BERMUDA HIGHBALL

1 Cube of Ice
¾ oz. Old Mr. Boston Dry Gin
¾ oz. Old Mr. Boston Five Star
  Brandy
¾ oz. Dry Vermouth
*Fill 8 oz. highball glass with ginger
ale or carbonated water. Add twist
of lemon peel, if desired, and stir.*

BERMUDA ROSE COCKTAIL

1¼ oz. Old Mr. Boston Dry Gin
¼ oz. Old Mr. Boston Apricot
  Flavored Brandy
¼ oz. Grenadine
*Shake well with cracked ice and
strain into 3 oz. cocktail glass.*

BETWEEN THE SHEETS COCKTAIL

Juice ¼ Lemon
½ oz. Old Mr. Boston Five Star
  Brandy
½ oz. Triple Sec
½ oz. Old Mr. Boston Imported
  Rum
*Shake well with cracked ice and
strain into 3 oz. cocktail glass.*

BIFFY COCKTAIL

Juice of ½ Lemon
½ oz. Swedish Punch
1½ oz. Old Mr. Boston Dry Gin
*Shake well with cracked ice and
strain into 3 oz. cocktail glass.*

BIJOU COCKTAIL

¾ oz. Old Mr. Boston Dry Gin
¾ oz. Green Chartreuse
¾ oz. Sweet Vermouth
1 Dash Orange Bitters
*Stir well with cracked ice and strain
into 3 oz. cocktail glass. Add cherry
on top.*

BILLY TAYLOR

Juice ½ Lime
2 Cubes of Ice
2 oz. Old Mr. Boston Dry Gin
*Fill 12 oz. Tom Collins glass with
carbonated water and stir gently.*

BIRD OF PARADISE FIZZ

Juice ½ Lemon
1 Teaspoon Powdered Sugar
White of 1 Egg
1 Teaspoon Grenadine
2 oz. Old Mr. Boston Dry Gin
*Shake well with cracked ice and
strain into 8 oz. highball glass. Fill
with carbonated water.*

BISHOP

Juice ¼ Lemon
Juice ¼ Orange
1 Teaspoon Powdered Sugar
*Shake well with cracked ice and
strain into 8 oz. highball glass. Add
cube of ice, fill with Burgundy and
stir well. Decorate with fruits.*

B

BITTERS HIGHBALL

1 Cube of Ice
¾ oz. Bitters
Fill 8 oz. highball glass with ginger ale or carbonated water. Add twist of lemon peel, if desired, and stir.

BLACK HAWK COCKTAIL

1¼ oz. Old Mr. Boston Whiskey*
1¼ oz. Old Mr. Boston Sloe Gin
Stir well with cracked ice and strain into 3 oz. cocktail glass. Serve with a cherry.

BLACK MAGIC

1½ oz. Old Mr. Boston Vodka
¾ oz. Expresso Coffee Liqueur
Dash of Lemon Juice.
Stir and serve in Old Fashioned cocktail glass with cubes of ice and twist of lemon peel.

BLACK RUSSIAN

Pour:
1½ oz. Old Mr. Boston Vodka
¾ oz. Kahlúa (Coffee Liqueur)
On ice cubes in Old Fashioned cocktail glass.

BLACK VELVET

5 oz. Stout
5 oz. Champagne
Pour very carefully into 12 oz. glass with cubes of ice and stir very gently.

BLARNEY STONE COCKTAIL

2 oz. Irish Whiskey
½ Teaspoon Absinthe Substitute
½ Teaspoon Curacao
¼ Teaspoon Maraschino
1 Dash Bitters
Shake well with cracked ice and strain into 3 oz. cocktail glass. Twist of orange peel and serve with an olive.

BLOOD AND SAND COCKTAIL

½ oz. Orange Juice
½ oz. Old Mr. Boston Scotch Whisky
½ oz. Old Mr. Boston Wild Cherry Flavored Brandy
½ oz. Sweet Vermouth
Shake well with cracked ice and strain into 3 oz. cocktail glass.

BLOOD BRONX COCKTAIL

1½ oz. Old Mr. Boston Dry Gin
¼ oz. Dry Vermouth
Juice of ¼ Blood Orange
Shake well with cracked ice and strain into 3 oz. cocktail glass.

BLOODHOUND COCKTAIL

½ oz. Dry Vermouth
½ oz. Sweet Vermouth
1 oz. Old Mr. Boston Dry Gin
2 or 3 crushed Strawberries
Shake well with cracked ice and strain into 3 oz. cocktail glass.

9

* Bourbon, Blended, Rye or Canadian.

BLOODY BLOODY MARY COCKTAIL

1½ oz. Old Mr. Boston Vodka
3 oz. Tomato Juice
Juice ½ Lemon
Pinch Salt, Pepper and Celery Salt
½ Teaspoon Worcestershire Sauce
¼ Teaspoon Powdered Sugar
Shake well with cracked ice and strain into 6 oz. Old Fashioned cocktail glass with cube of ice. Decorate with sprig of fresh mint.

BLOODY MARY COCKTAIL

1½ oz. Old Mr. Boston Vodka
1½ oz. Tomato Juice
1 Dash Lemon Juice
Shake well with cracked ice and strain into Old Fashioned cocktail glass with cube of ice.

BLUE BLAZER

Use two large silver-plated mugs, with handles.
2½ oz. Old Mr. Boston Whiskey*
2½ oz. Boiling Water
Put the whiskey into one mug, and the boiling water into the other. Ignite the whiskey and, while blazing, mix both ingredients by pouring them four or five times from one mug to the other. If well done, this will have the appearance of a continued stream of liquid fire.
Sweeten with 1 teaspoon of Powdered Sugar and serve with a piece of lemon peel. Serve in 4 oz. hot whiskey glass.

BLUE DEVIL COCKTAIL

1 oz. Old Mr. Boston Dry Gin
Juice ½ Lemon or 1 Lime
½ oz. Maraschino
½ Teaspoon Creme de Yvette
Shake well with cracked ice and strain into 3 oz. cocktail glass.

BLUE MONDAY COCKTAIL

1½ oz. Old Mr. Boston Vodka
¾ oz. Triple Sec
1 Dash Blue Vegetable Coloring
Stir well with cracked ice and strain into 3 oz. cocktail glass.

BLUE MOON COCKTAIL

1½ oz. Old Mr. Boston Dry Gin
¾ oz. Creme de Yvette
Stir well with cracked ice and strain into 3 oz. cocktail glass. Add twist of lemon peel and drop in glass.

BOBBY BURNS COCKTAIL

1¼ oz. Sweet Vermouth
1¼ oz. Old Mr. Boston Scotch Whisky
1 Teaspoon Benedictine
Stir well with cracked ice and strain into 3 oz. cocktail glass. Add twist of lemon peel and drop in glass.

BOLERO COCKTAIL

1½ oz. Old Mr. Boston Imported Rum
¾ oz. Apple Brandy
¼ Teaspoon Sweet Vermouth
Stir well with cracked ice and strain into 3 oz. cocktail glass.

* *Bourbon, Blended, Rye or Canadian.*

Bronze Label Kentucky Straight Bourbon 86 Proof ▶

BOLO COCKTAIL

2 oz. Old Mr. Boston Imported Rum
Juice of ½ Lime
Juice of ¼ Orange
1 Teaspoon Powdered Sugar
Shake well with cracked ice and strain into 4 oz. cocktail glass.

BOMBAY COCKTAIL

½ oz. Dry Vermouth
½ oz. Sweet Vermouth
1 oz. Old Mr. Boston Five Star Brandy
¼ Teaspoon Absinthe Substitute
½ Teaspoon Curacao
Stir well with cracked ice and strain into 3 oz. cocktail glass.

BOMBAY PUNCH

Juice of 1 Dozen Lemons
Add enough powdered sugar to sweeten. Place large block of ice in punch bowl and stir. Then add:
1 qt. Old Mr. Boston Five Star Brandy
1 qt. Sherry Wine
¼ pt. Maraschino
¼ pt. Curacao
4 qts. Champagne
2 qts. Carbonated Water
Some prefer to add the strained contents of a pot of tea. Stir well and decorate with fruits in season. Serve in 4 oz. Punch glasses.

BOSTON BULLET

See *Special Martini Section* on pages 116 and 117.

BOSTON COCKTAIL

¾ oz. Old Mr. Boston Dry Gin
¾ oz. Old Mr. Boston Apricot Flavored Brandy
Juice of ¼ Lemon
¼ oz. Grenadine
Shake well with cracked ice and strain into 3 oz. cocktail glass.

BOSTON COOLER

Into 12 oz. Tom Collins glass, put:
Juice ½ Lemon
1 Teaspoon Powdered Sugar
2 oz. Carbonated Water
Stir. Then fill glass with cracked ice and add:
2 oz. Old Mr. Boston Imported Rum
Fill with carbonated water or ginger ale and stir again. Insert spiral of orange or lemon peel (or both) and dangle end over rim of glass.

BOSTON SIDE CAR COCKTAIL

¾ oz. Old Mr. Boston Five Star Brandy
¾ oz. Old Mr. Boston Imported Rum
¾ oz. Triple Sec
Juice ½ Lime
Shake well with cracked ice and strain into 3 oz. cocktail glass.

Boston Sour

Juice ½ Lemon
1 Teaspoon Powdered Sugar
2 oz. Old Mr. Boston Whiskey*
White of 1 Egg
Shake well with cracked ice and strain into 8 oz. highball glass. Then add cube of ice, fill with carbonated water and decorate with half-slice of lemon and a cherry.

Bourbon Highball

1 Cube of Ice
2 oz. Old Mr. Boston Kentucky
   Bourbon Whiskey
Fill 8 oz. highball glass with ginger ale or carbonated water. Add twist of lemon peel, if desired, and stir.

Brandy and Soda

2 Cubes of Ice
2 oz. Old Mr. Boston Five Star
   Brandy
6 oz. Carbonated Water
Serve in 12 oz. Tom Collins glass and stir.

Brandy Blazer

1 Lump Sugar
1 Piece Orange Peel
1 Piece Lemon Peel
2 oz. Old Mr. Boston Five Star
   Brandy
Use Old Fashioned cocktail glass. Light with a match, stir with long spoon for a few seconds and strain into a hot whiskey glass.

Brandy Cobbler

Dissolve: 1 teaspoon powdered sugar in 2 oz. carbonated water; then fill 10 oz. goblet with shaved ice.
Add 2 oz. Old Mr. Boston Five Star
   Brandy
Stir well and decorate with fruits in season. Serve with straws.

Brandy Cocktail

2 oz. Old Mr. Boston Five Star
   Brandy
¼ Teaspoon Simple Syrup
2 Dashes Bitters
Twist of Lemon Peel
Stir well with cracked ice and strain into 3 oz. cocktail glass.

Brandy Collins

Juice ½ Lemon
1 Teaspoon Powdered Sugar
2 oz. Old Mr. Boston Five Star
   Brandy
Shake well with cracked ice and strain into 12 oz. Tom Collins glass. Add several cubes of ice, fill with carbonated water and stir. Decorate with slice of orange, lemon and a cherry. Serve with straws.

* *Bourbon, Blended, Rye or Canadian.*

B

Brandy Crusta Cocktail

Moisten the edge of 4 oz. cocktail glass with lemon and dip into sugar. Cut the rind of half a lemon in a spiral, and place in glass.
1 Teaspoon Maraschino
1 Dash Bitters
1 Teaspoon Lemon Juice
½ oz. Curacao
2 oz. Old Mr. Boston Five Star Brandy
Stir above ingredients in mixing glass and strain into glass prepared as above. Add slice of orange.

Brandy Daisy

Juice of ½ Lemon
½ Teaspoon Powdered Sugar
1 Teaspoon Raspberry Syrup or Grenadine
2 oz. Old Mr. Boston Five Star Brandy
Shake well with cracked ice and strain into Stein or 8 oz. metal cup. Add cube of ice and decorate with fruit.

Brandy Eggnog

1 Egg
1 Teaspoon Powdered Sugar
2 oz. Old Mr. Boston Five Star Brandy
Fill glass with Milk
Shake well with cracked ice and strain into 12 oz. Tom Collins glass. Grate nutmeg on top.

Brandy Fix

Juice ½ Lemon
1 Teaspoon Powdered Sugar
1 Teaspoon Water
Stir. Then fill glass with shaved ice.
2½ oz. Old Mr. Boston Five Star Brandy
Use 8 oz. highball glass. Stir well. Add slice of lemon. Serve with straws.

Brandy Fizz

Juice ½ Lemon
1 Teaspoon Powdered Sugar
2 oz. Old Mr. Boston Five Star Brandy
Shake well with cracked ice and strain into 7 oz. highball glass. Fill with carbonated water.

Brandy Flip

1 Egg
1 Teaspoon Powdered Sugar
1½ oz. Old Mr. Boston Five Star Brandy
2 Teaspoons Sweet Cream (if desired)
Shake well with cracked ice and strain into 5 oz. flip glass. Grate a little nutmeg on top.

Brandy Gump Cocktail

1½ oz. Old Mr. Boston Five Star Brandy
Juice of ½ Lemon
½ Teaspoon Grenadine
Shake well with cracked ice and strain into 3 oz. cocktail glass.

14

B

BRANDY HIGHBALL

1 Cube of Ice
2 oz. Old Mr. Boston Five Star
   Brandy
*Fill 8 oz. highball glass with ginger
ale or carbonated water. Add twist
of lemon peel, if desired, and stir
gently.*

BRANDY JULEP

Into 12 oz. Tom Collins glass put:
1 Teaspoon Powdered Sugar
5 or 6 Sprigs Fresh Mint
2½ oz. Old Mr. Boston Five Star
   Brandy
*Then fill glass with finely shaved ice,
and stir until mint rises to top, being
careful not to bruise mint. (Do not
hold glass with hand while stirring.)
Decorate with slice of pineapple, orange, lemon and a cherry. Serve with
straws.*

BRANDY MILK PUNCH

1 Teaspoon Powdered Sugar
2 oz. Old Mr. Boston Five Star
   Brandy
½ Pint Milk
*Shake well with cracked ice, strain
into 12 oz. Tom Collins glass and
grate nutmeg on top.*

BRANDY PUNCH

Juice of 1 Dozen Lemons
Juice of 4 Oranges
Add enough sugar to sweeten.
8 oz. Grenadine
1 qt. Carbonated Water
*Place large block of ice in punch
bowl and stir well. Then add:*
½ Pint Curacao
2 qts. Old Mr. Boston Five Star
   Brandy
*Some prefer to add the strained con-
tents of a pot of tea. Stir well and
decorate with fruits in season. Serve
in 4 oz. punch glasses.*

BRANDY SANGAREE

*Dissolve ½ teaspoon powdered sugar
in 1 teaspoon of water.*
2 oz. Old Mr. Boston Five Star
   Brandy
2 Cubes of Ice
*Serve in 8 oz. highball glass. Fill
balance with soda water. Stir, leaving enough room on which to float a
tablespoon of Port Wine. Sprinkle
lightly with nutmeg.*

BRANDY SLING

*Dissolve 1 Teaspoon Powdered Sugar
in Teaspoon of Water and Juice ½
Lemon.*
2 oz. Old Mr. Boston Five Star
   Brandy
2 Cubes of Ice
*Serve in Old Fashioned cocktail glass
and stir. Twist of lemon peel and
drop in glass.*

B

Brandy Smash

Muddle 1 Lump of Sugar with
1 oz. Carbonated Water and
4 Sprigs of Green Mint
2 oz. Old Mr. Boston Five Star
Brandy
*Add a cube of ice. Stir and decorate
with a slice of Orange and a cherry.
Twist lemon peel on top. Use Old
Fashioned cocktail glass.*

Brandy Sour

Juice ½ Lemon
½ Teaspoon Powdered Sugar
2 oz. Old Mr. Boston Five Star
Brandy
*Shake well with cracked ice and
strain into 6 oz. sour glass. Decorate
with a half-slice of lemon and a
cherry.*

Brandy Squirt

1½ oz. Old Mr. Boston Five Star
Brandy
1 Tablespoon Powdered Sugar
1 Teaspoon Raspberry Syrup or
Grenadine
*Shake well with cracked ice and
strain into 8 oz. highball glass and
fill with carbonated water. Decorate
with cubes of pineapple and strawberries.*

Brandy Swizzle

Made same as Gin Swizzle *(see
page 43), using* 2 oz. Old Mr. Boston Five Star Brandy.

Brandy Toddy

Use Old Fashioned cocktail glass.
½ Teaspoon Powdered Sugar
2 Teaspoons Water *and stir.*
2 oz. Old Mr. Boston Five Star
Brandy
1 Lump of Ice
*Stir again and twist lemon peel on
top.*

Brandy Toddy (hot)

*Put lump of sugar into hot whiskey
glass and fill two-thirds with boiling
water. Add* 2 oz. Old Mr. Boston
Five Star Brandy. *Stir and decorate
with slice of lemon. Grate nutmeg on
top.*

Brandy Vermouth Cocktail

½ oz. Sweet Vermouth
2 oz. Old Mr. Boston Five Star
Brandy
1 Dash Bitters
*Stir well with cracked ice and strain
into 3 oz. cocktail glass.*

Brazil Cocktail

1¼ oz. Dry Vermouth
1¼ oz. Sherry Wine
1 Dash Bitters
¼ Teaspoon Absinthe Substitute
*Stir well with cracked ice and strain
into 3 oz. cocktail glass.*

Breakfast Eggnog

1 Egg
½ oz. Curacao
2 oz. Old Mr. Boston Apricot Flavored Brandy
*Fill glass with milk. Shake well with
cracked ice and strain into 12 oz.
Tom Collins glass. Grate nutmeg on
top.*

B

Brighton Punch

¾ oz. Old Mr. Boston Whiskey*
¾ oz. Cognac
¾ oz. Benedictine
Juice ½ Orange
Juice ½ Lemon
Shake well and pour into 12 oz. Tom Collins glass filled with shaved ice. Then fill with carbonated water and stir gently. Serve with straws. Old Mr. Boston Five Star Brandy may be substituted for Cognac.

Broken Spur Cocktail

¾ oz. Sweet Vermouth
1½ oz. Port Wine
¼ Teaspoon Curacao
Stir well with cracked ice and strain into 3 oz. cocktail glass.

Bronx Cocktail

1 oz. Old Mr. Boston Dry Gin
½ oz. Dry Vermouth
½ oz. Sweet Vermouth
Juice ¼ Orange
Shake well with cracked ice and strain into 3 oz. cocktail glass. Serve with slice of orange.

Bronx Cocktail (dry)

1 oz. Old Mr. Boston Dry Gin
1 oz. Dry Vermouth
Juice ¼ Orange
Shake well with cracked ice and strain into 3 oz. cocktail glass. Serve with slice of orange.

Bronx Golden Cocktail

Made same as Bronx Cocktail, adding the yolk of one egg. Use 4 oz. cocktail glass.

Bronx Silver Cocktail

Juice of ¼ Orange
White of 1 Egg
½ oz. Dry Vermouth
1 oz. Old Mr. Boston Dry Gin
Shake well with cracked ice and strain into 4 oz. cocktail glass.

Bronx Terrace Cocktail

1½ oz. Old Mr. Boston Dry Gin
1½ oz. Dry Vermouth
Juice of ½ Lime
Shake well with cracked ice and strain into 3 oz. cocktail glass. Add a cherry.

Brown Cocktail

¾ oz. Old Mr. Boston Dry Gin
¾ oz. Old Mr. Boston Imported Rum
¾ oz. Dry Vermouth
Stir well with cracked ice and strain into 3 oz. cocktail glass.

Bucks Fizz

¼ Glass Orange Juice
Fill with Champagne. Use 12 oz. Tom Collins glass and stir very gently.

Bulldog Cocktail

1¼ oz. Old Mr. Boston Wild Cherry Flavored Brandy
¾ oz. Old Mr. Boston Dry Gin
Juice of ½ Lime
Shake well with cracked ice and strain into 3 oz. cocktail glass.

Bulldog Highball

1 Cube of Ice
Juice of ½ Orange
2 oz. Old Mr. Boston Dry Gin
Fill 8 oz. highball glass with ginger ale and stir.

* *Bourbon, Blended, Rye or Canadian.*

Straight Bourbon 80 Proof ▶

C

BULL'S EYE

1 oz. Old Mr. Boston Five Star Brandy
2 oz. Hard Cider
1 Cube of Ice
Fill 8 oz. highball glass with ginger ale and stir.

BULL'S MILK

1 Teaspoon Powdered Sugar
1 oz. Old Mr. Boston Imported Rum
1½ oz. Old Mr. Boston Five Star Brandy
½ Pint Milk
Shake well with cracked ice and strain into 12 oz. Tom Collins glass. Grate nutmeg and pinch of cinnamon on top.

BURGUNDY BISHOP

Juice ¼ Lemon
1 Teaspoon Powdered Sugar
1 oz. Old Mr. Boston Imported Rum
Shake well and strain into 8 oz. highball glass and fill with Burgundy and stir. Decorate with fruits.

BUTTON HOOK COCKTAIL

½ oz. Old Mr. Boston Creme de Menthe (White)
½ oz. Old Mr. Boston Apricot Flavored Brandy
½ oz. Absinthe Substitute
½ oz. Old Mr. Boston Five Star Brandy
Shake well with cracked ice and strain into 3 oz. cocktail glass.

CABARET COCKTAIL

1½ oz. Old Mr. Boston Dry Gin
2 Dashes Bitters
½ Teaspoon Dry Vermouth
¼ Teaspoon Benedictine
Stir well with cracked ice and strain into 3 oz. cocktail glass. Serve with a cherry.

CABLEGRAM HIGHBALL

Juice ½ Lemon
1 Teaspoon Powdered Sugar
2 oz. Old Mr. Boston Whiskey*
Stir well with cracked ice and fill with ginger ale. Use 8 oz. highball glass.

* *Bourbon, Blended, Rye or Canadian*

C

CAFÉ DE PARIS COCKTAIL

White of 1 Egg
1 Teaspoon Absinthe Substitute
1 Teaspoon Sweet Cream
1½ oz. Old Mr. Boston Dry Gin
Shake well with cracked ice and strain into 4 oz. cocktail glass.

CAFÉ ROYALE

1 Cup Hot Black Coffee
Put cube of sugar, well soaked with Old Mr. Boston Five Star Brandy, in teaspoon and hold so that it will rest on top of coffee and ignite and hold until flame burns out. Drop contents in coffee.

CALIFORNIA LEMONADE

Juice 1 Lemon
Juice 1 Lime
3 Teaspoons Powdered Sugar
2 oz. Old Mr. Boston Whiskey*
¼ Teaspoon Grenadine
Shake well with cracked ice and strain into 12 oz. Tom Collins glass filled with shaved ice. Fill with carbonated water and decorate with slice of orange, lemon, and a cherry. Serve with straws.

CAMERON'S KICK COCKTAIL

¾ oz. Old Mr. Boston Scotch Whisky
¼ oz. Irish Whiskey
Juice ¼ Lemon
2 Dashes Orange Bitters
Shake well with cracked ice and strain into 3 oz. cocktail glass.

CAPE CODDER

1½ oz. Old Mr. Boston Vodka or Old Mr. Boston Imported Rum
3 oz. Cranberry Juice
Juice ½ Lime (if desired)
May be served on the rocks in Old Fashioned Cocktail glass or in 8 oz. highball glass with cubes of ice and carbonated water. Stir.

CARDINAL PUNCH

Juice of 1 Dozen Lemons
Add enough Powdered Sugar to sweeten. Place large block of ice in punch bowl and stir well. Then add:
1 pt. Old Mr. Boston Five Star Brandy
1 pt. Old Mr. Boston Imported Rum
1 pt. Champagne
2 qts. Claret
1 qt. Carbonated Water
½ pt. Sweet Vermouth
Some prefer to add the strained contents of a pot of tea. Stir well and decorate with fruits in season. Serve in 4 oz. punch glasses.

CARROL COCKTAIL

1½ oz. Old Mr. Boston Five Star Brandy
¾ oz. Sweet Vermouth
Stir well with cracked ice and strain into 3 oz. cocktail glass. Serve with a cherry.

21

* *Bourbon, Blended, Rye or Canadian.*

C

Casino Cocktail

2 Dashes Orange Bitters
¼ Teaspoon Maraschino
¼ Teaspoon Lemon Juice
2 oz. Old Mr. Boston Dry Gin
Shake well with cracked ice and strain into 3 oz. cocktail glass. Serve with a cherry.

Champagne Cocktail

Spiral Rind of ½ Lemon
1 Lump Sugar
2 Dashes Bitters
Use 6 oz. Champagne glass. Fill with Champagne.

Champagne Cup

Use Large Glass Pitcher
4 Teaspoons Powdered Sugar
6 oz. Carbonated Water
½ oz. Triple Sec
½ oz. Curacao
2 oz. Old Mr. Boston Five Star Brandy
Fill pitcher with cubes of ice. Add 1 pint of Champagne. Stir well and decorate with as many fruits as available and also rind of cucumber inserted on each side of pitcher. Top with small bunch of mint sprigs. Serve in 5 oz. claret glass.

Champagne Punch

Juice of 1 Dozen Lemons
Add enough Powdered Sugar to sweeten. Place large block of ice in punch bowl and stir well. Then add:
½ pt. Maraschino
½ pt. Curacao
1 pt. Old Mr. Boston Five Star Brandy
2 qts. Champagne
1 qt. Carbonated Water
Some prefer to add the strained contents of a pot of tea. Stir well and decorate with fruits in season. Serve in 4 oz. punch glasses.

Champagne Velvet

See **Black Velvet** on page 9.

Champs Élysées Cocktail

1 oz. Cognac
½ oz. Yellow Chartreuse
Juice of ¼ Lemon
½ Teaspoon Powdered Sugar
1 Dash Bitters
Shake well with cracked ice and strain into 3 oz. cocktail glass. Old Mr. Boston Five Star Brandy may be substituted for Cognac.

Charles Cocktail

1¼ oz. Sweet Vermouth
1¼ oz. Old Mr. Boston Five Star Brandy
1 Dash Bitters
Stir well with cracked ice and strain into 3 oz. cocktail glass.

C

CHELSEA SIDE CAR COCKTAIL

Juice of ¼ Lemon
¼ oz. Triple Sec
¼ oz. Old Mr. Boston Dry Gin
*Shake well with cracked ice and
strain into 3 oz. cocktail glass.*

CHERRY BLOSSOM COCKTAIL

1 oz. Old Mr. Boston Wild Cherry
Flavored Brandy
1 oz. Old Mr. Boston Five Star
Brandy
¼ Teaspoon Curacao
¼ Teaspoon Lemon Juice
¼ Teaspoon Grenadine
*Shake well with cracked ice and
strain into 3 oz. cocktail glass.*

CHERRY FIZZ

Juice ½ Lemon
2 oz. Old Mr. Boston Wild Cherry
Flavored Brandy
*Shake well with cracked ice and
strain into 7 oz. highball glass. Fill
with carbonated water and decorate
with a cherry.*

CHERRY FLIP

1 Egg
1 Teaspoon Powdered Sugar
1½ oz. Old Mr. Boston Wild
Cherry Flavored Brandy
2 Teaspoons Sweet Cream
(if desired)
*Shake well with cracked ice and
strain into 5 oz. flip glass. Grate a
little nutmeg on top.*

CHERRY SLING

2 Cubes of Ice
2 oz. Old Mr. Boston Wild Cherry
Flavored Brandy
Juice ½ Lemon
*Serve in Old Fashioned cocktail glass
and stir. Twist of lemon peel and
drop in glass.*

CHICAGO COCKTAIL

2 oz. Old Mr. Boston Five Star
Brandy
1 Dash Bitters
¼ Teaspoon Curacao
*Stir well with cracked ice and strain
into 3 oz. cocktail glass. Frost glass
by rubbing slice of lemon around
rim and then dip in powdered sugar.*

CHICAGO FIZZ

Juice ½ Lemon
1 Teaspoon Powdered Sugar
White of 1 Egg
1 oz. Port Wine
1 oz. Old Mr. Boston Imported
Rum
*Shake well with cracked ice and
strain into 7 oz. highball glass. Fill
with carbonated water and stir.*

CHINESE COCKTAIL

½ oz. Grenadine
1½ oz. Jamaica Rum
1 Dash Bitters
1 Teaspoon Maraschino
1 Teaspoon Curacao
*Shake well with cracked ice and
strain into 3 oz. cocktail glass.*

CHOCOLATE COCKTAIL

1½ oz. Port Wine
¼ oz. Yellow Chartreuse
Yolk of 1 Egg
1 Teaspoon Powdered Sugar
Shake well with cracked ice and strain into 4 oz. cocktail glass.

CHOCOLATE DAISY

Juice ½ Lemon
½ Teaspoon Powdered Sugar
1 Teaspoon Raspberry Syrup or Grenadine
1½ oz. Old Mr. Boston Five Star Brandy
1½ oz. Port Wine
Shake well with cracked ice and strain into stein or 8 oz. metal cup. Add cube of ice and decorate with fruit.

CHOCOLATE FLIP

1 Egg
1 Teaspoon of Powdered Sugar
¾ oz. Old Mr. Boston Sloe Gin
¾ oz. Old Mr. Boston Five Star Brandy
2 Teaspoons Sweet Cream (if desired)
Shake well with cracked ice and strain into 5 oz. flip glass. Grate a little nutmeg on top.

CHOCOLATE SOLDIER COCKTAIL

Juice ½ Lime
¾ oz. Dubonnet
1½ oz. Old Mr. Boston Dry Gin
Shake well with cracked ice and strain into 3 oz. cocktail glass.

CHRISTMAS YULE EGGNOG

Beat the yolks and whites of 1 Dozen Eggs separately and then pour together and add:
1 Pinch Baking Soda
6 oz. Old Mr. Boston Imported Rum
2 lbs. Granulated Sugar
Beat into stiff batter. Then add:
1 qt. Milk
1 qt. Sweet Cream
2 qts. Old Mr. Boston Whiskey*
Stir. Set in refrigerator over night. Before serving, stir again, and serve in 4 oz. punch glasses, and grate nutmeg on top.

CIDER CUP

Use Large Glass Pitcher
4 Teaspoons Powdered Sugar
6 oz. Carbonated Water
½ oz. Triple Sec
½ oz. Curacao
2 oz. Old Mr. Boston Five Star Brandy
Fill pitcher with cubes of ice. Add 1 pint of cider. Stir well and decorate with as many fruits as available and also rind of cucumber inserted on each side of pitcher. Top with small bunch of mint sprigs. Serve in 5 oz. claret glasses.

CIDER EGGNOG

1 Egg
1 Teaspoon Powdered Sugar
¼ pt. Milk
Shake well with cracked ice and strain into 12 oz. Tom Collins glass. Then fill glass with sweet cider and stir. Grate nutmeg on top.

* Bourbon, Blended, Rye or Canadian

CLAM AND TOMATO COCKTAIL

1½ oz. Old Mr. Boston Vodka
1 oz. Clam Juice
3 oz. Tomato Juice
Shake well with cracked ice, strain, and serve on the rocks in large Old Fashioned glass.

CLARET COBBLER

Dissolve: 1 teaspoon powdered sugar in 2 oz. carbonated water; then add 3 oz. Claret. Fill 10 oz. goblet with shaved ice and stir. Decorate with fruits in season. Serve with straws.

CLARET CUP

Use Large Glass Pitcher
4 Teaspoons Powdered Sugar
6 oz. Carbonated Water
½ oz. Triple Sec
½ oz. Curacao
2 oz. Old Mr. Boston Five Star
  Brandy
Fill pitcher with cubes of ice. Add 1 pint of Claret. Stir well and decorate with as many fruits as available and also rind of cucumber inserted on each side of pitcher. Top with small bunch of mint sprigs. Serve in 5 oz. claret glass.

CLARET PUNCH

Juice of 1 Dozen Lemons
Add enough powdered sugar to sweeten. Place large block of ice in punch bowl and stir well. Then add:
½ pt. Curacao
1 pt. Old Mr. Boston Five Star
  Brandy
3 qts. Claret
1 qt. Carbonated Water
Some prefer to add the strained contents of a pot of tea. Stir well and decorate with fruits in season. Serve in 4 oz. punch glasses.

CLARIDGE COCKTAIL

¾ oz. Old Mr. Boston Dry Gin
¾ oz. Dry Vermouth
½ oz. Old Mr. Boston Apricot
  Flavored Brandy
½ oz. Triple Sec
Stir well with cracked ice and strain into 3 oz. cocktail glass.

CLASSIC COCKTAIL

Juice of ¼ Lemon
¼ oz. Curacao
¼ oz. Maraschino
1 oz. Old Mr. Boston Five Star
  Brandy
Shake well with cracked ice and strain into 3 oz. cocktail glass. Frost rim of glass by rubbing with lemon and dipping in powdered sugar.

CLOVE COCKTAIL

1 oz. Sweet Vermouth
½ oz. Old Mr. Boston Sloe Gin
½ oz. Muscatel Wine
Stir well with cracked ice and strain into 3 oz. cocktail glass.

C

Clover Club Cocktail

Juice ½ Lemon
2 Teaspoons Grenadine
White of 1 Egg
1½ oz. Old Mr. Boston Dry Gin
Shake well with cracked ice and strain into 4 oz. cocktail glass.

Clover Leaf Cocktail

Juice 1 Lime
2 Teaspoons Grenadine
White of 1 Egg
1½ oz. Old Mr. Boston Dry Gin
Shake well with cracked ice and strain into 4 oz. cocktail glass. Serve with mint leaf on top.

Club Cocktail

1½ oz. Old Mr. Boston Dry Gin
¾ oz. Sweet Vermouth
Stir well with cracked ice and strain into 3 oz. cocktail glass. Add a cherry or olive.

Cobblers

See Index on page 139 for complete list of COBBLER recipes.

Coffee Cocktail

1 Egg
1 Teaspoon Powdered Sugar
1 oz. Port Wine
1 oz. Old Mr. Boston Five Star Brandy
Shake well with cracked ice and strain into 5 oz. cocktail glass. Grate nutmeg on top.

Coffee Flip

1 Egg
1 Teaspoon Powdered Sugar
1 oz. Old Mr. Boston Five Star Brandy
1 oz. Port Wine
2 Teaspoons Sweet Cream (if desired)
Shake well with cracked ice and strain into 5 oz. flip glass. Grate a little nutmeg on top.

Cognac Highball

1 Cube of Ice
2 oz. Cognac
Fill 8 oz. highball glass with ginger ale or carbonated water. Add twist of lemon peel, if desired, and stir gently.

Cold Deck Cocktail

½ oz. Old Mr. Boston Creme de Menthe (White)
½ oz. Sweet Vermouth
1 oz. Old Mr. Boston Five Star Brandy
Stir well with cracked ice and strain into 3 oz. cocktail glass.

Collins

See Index on page 139 for complete list of COLLINS recipes.

Colonial Cocktail

½ oz. Grapefruit Juice
1 Teaspoon Maraschino
1½ oz. Old Mr. Boston Dry Gin
Shake well with cracked ice and strain into 3 oz. cocktail glass. Serve with an olive.

COMMODORE COCKTAIL

Juice ½ Lime or ¼ Lemon
1 Teaspoon Powdered Sugar
2 Dashes Orange Bitters
1½ oz. Old Mr. Boston Whiskey*
Shake well with cracked ice and strain into 3 oz. cocktail glass.

COOLERS

See Index on page 140 for complete list of COOLER *recipes.*

COOPERSTOWN COCKTAIL

½ oz. Dry Vermouth
½ oz. Sweet Vermouth
1 oz. Old Mr. Boston Dry Gin
2 Sprigs Fresh Mint
Shake well with cracked ice and strain into 3 oz. cocktail glass.

CORNELL COCKTAIL

½ Teaspoon Lemon Juice
1 Teaspoon Maraschino
White of 1 Egg
1½ oz. Old Mr. Boston Dry Gin
Shake well with cracked ice and strain into 4 oz. cocktail glass.

CORONATION COCKTAIL

¾ oz. Old Mr. Boston Dry Gin
¾ oz. Dubonnet
¾ oz. Dry Vermouth
Stir well with cracked ice and strain into 3 oz. cocktail glass.

COUNTRY CLUB COOLER

Into 12 oz. Tom Collins glass, put:
½ Teaspoon Grenadine
2 oz. Carbonated Water *and stir.*
Fill glass with cracked ice and add:
2 oz. Dry Vermouth
Fill with carbonated water or ginger ale and stir again. Insert spiral of orange or lemon peel (or both) and dangle end over rim of glass.

COWBOY COCKTAIL

1½ oz. Old Mr. Boston Whiskey*
½ oz. Sweet Cream
Shake well with cracked ice and strain into 3 oz. cocktail glass.

CREAM FIZZ

Juice ½ Lemon
1 Teaspoon Powdered Sugar
2 oz. Old Mr. Boston Dry Gin
1 Teaspoon Fresh Cream
Shake well with cracked ice and strain into 8 oz. highball glass. Fill with carbonated water and stir.

CREAM PUFF

2 oz. Old Mr. Boston Imported Rum
1 oz. Sweet Cream
½ Teaspoon Powdered Sugar
Shake well with cracked ice and strain into 8 oz. highball glass. Fill with carbonated water and stir.

* *Bourbon, Blended, Rye or Canadian.*

C

CREME DE GIN COCKTAIL

1½ oz. Old Mr. Boston Dry Gin
½ oz. Old Mr. Boston Creme de Menthe (white)
White of 1 Egg
2 Teaspoons Lemon Juice
2 Teaspoons Orange Juice
Shake well with cracked ice and strain into 4 oz. cocktail glass.

CREME DE MENTHE FRAPPE

Fill cocktail glass up to brim with shaved ice. Add Old Mr. Boston Creme de Menthe (green). *Serve with two short straws.*

CREOLE LADY COCKTAIL

1¼ oz. Old Mr. Boston Whiskey*
1¼ oz. Madeira Wine
1 Teaspoon Grenadine
Stir well with cracked ice and strain into 3 oz. cocktail glass. Serve with 1 green and 1 red cherry.

CRIMSON COCKTAIL

1½ oz. Old Mr. Boston Dry Gin
2 Teaspoons Lemon Juice
1 Teaspoon Grenadine
Shake well with cracked ice and strain into 3 oz. cocktail glass, leaving enough room on top to float ¾ oz. Port Wine.

CRYSTAL SLIPPER COCKTAIL

½ oz. Creme de Yvette
2 Dashes Orange Bitters
1½ oz. Old Mr. Boston Dry Gin
Stir well with cracked ice and strain into 3 oz. cocktail glass.

CUBA LIBRE

Juice ½ Lime
Drop rind in glass.
2 oz. Old Mr. Boston Imported Rum
2 Cubes of Ice
Fill glass with any cola. Use 10 oz. glass and stir well.

CUBAN COCKTAIL No. 1

Juice of ½ Lime
½ Teaspoon Powdered Sugar
2 oz. Old Mr. Boston Imported Rum
Shake well with cracked ice and strain into 3 oz. cocktail glass.

CUBAN COCKTAIL No. 2

Juice of ½ Lime or ¼ Lemon
½ oz. Old Mr. Boston Apricot Flavored Brandy
1½ oz. Old Mr. Boston Five Star Brandy
1 Teaspoon Old Mr. Boston Imported Rum
Shake well with cracked ice and strain into 3 oz. cocktail glass.

CUBAN SPECIAL COCKTAIL

½ oz. Pineapple Juice
Juice ½ Lime
1 oz. Old Mr. Boston Imported Rum
½ Teaspoon Curacao
Shake well with cracked ice and strain into 3 oz. cocktail glass. Decorate with stick of pineapple and a cherry.

CUPS

See Index on page 140 for complete list of CUP *recipes.*

29

* *Bourbon, Blended, Rye or Canadian.*

Daiquiri Cocktail

Juice 1 Lime
1 Teaspoon Powdered Sugar
1½ oz. Old Mr. Boston Imported
    Rum
*Shake well with cracked ice and
strain into 3 oz. cocktail glass.*

Daisies

*See Index on page 141 for complete
list of* Daisy *recipes.*

Damn-the-Weather Cocktail

1 Teaspoon Curacao
½ oz. Orange Juice
½ oz. Sweet Vermouth
1 oz. Old Mr. Boston Dry Gin
*Shake well with cracked ice and
strain into 3 oz. cocktail glass.*

Darb Cocktail

1 Teaspoon Lemon Juice
¾ oz. Dry Vermouth
¾ oz. Old Mr. Boston Dry Gin
¾ oz. Old Mr. Boston Apricot
    Flavored Brandy
*Shake well with cracked ice and
strain into 3 oz. cocktail glass.*

Deauville Cocktail

Juice of ¼ Lemon
½ oz. Old Mr. Boston Five Star
    Brandy
½ oz. Apple Brandy
½ oz. Triple Sec
*Shake well with cracked ice and
strain into 3 oz. cocktail glass.*

Deep Sea Cocktail

1 oz. Dry Vermouth
¼ Teaspoon Absinthe Substitute
1 Dash Orange Bitters
1 oz. Old Mr. Boston Dry Gin
*Stir well with cracked ice and strain
into 3 oz. cocktail glass.*

Dempsey Cocktail

1 oz. Old Mr. Boston Dry Gin
1 oz. Apple Brandy
½ Teaspoon Absinthe Substitute
½ Teaspoon Grenadine
*Stir well with cracked ice and strain
into 3 oz. cocktail glass.*

D

DERBY FIZZ

Juice ½ Lemon
1 Teaspoon Powdered Sugar
1 Egg
2 oz. Old Mr. Boston Scotch
    Whisky
1 Teaspoon Curacao
Shake well with cracked ice and strain into 8 oz. highball glass. Fill with carbonated water and stir.

DEVIL'S COCKTAIL

½ Teaspoon Lemon Juice
1¼ oz. Port Wine
1¼ oz. Dry Vermouth
Stir well with cracked ice and strain into 3 oz. cocktail glass.

DIAMOND FIZZ

Juice ½ Lemon
1 Teaspoon Powdered Sugar
2 oz. Old Mr. Boston Dry Gin
Shake well with cracked ice and strain into 7 oz. highball glass. Fill with champagne and stir gently.

DIANA COCKTAIL

Fill 3 oz. cocktail glass with shaved ice, then fill ¾ full with Old Mr. Boston Creme de Menthe (white) *and float* Old Mr. Boston Five Star Brandy *on top.*

DILLATINI COCKTAIL

See Special Martini Section on pages 116 and 117.

DINAH COCKTAIL

Juice of ¼ Lemon
½ Teaspoon Powdered Sugar
1½ oz. Old Mr. Boston Whiskey*
2 or 3 Sprigs Fresh Mint
Shake very well with cracked ice and strain into 3 oz. cocktail glass. Serve with a mint leaf.

DIPLOMAT COCKTAIL

1½ oz. Dry Vermouth
½ oz. Sweet Vermouth
2 Dashes Bitters
½ Teaspoon Maraschino
Stir well with cracked ice and strain into 3 oz. cocktail glass. Serve with ½ slice of lemon and a cherry.

DIXIE COCKTAIL

Juice of ¼ Orange
½ oz. Absinthe Substitute
½ oz. Dry Vermouth
1 oz. Old Mr. Boston Dry Gin
Shake well with cracked ice and strain into 4 oz. cocktail glass.

DIXIE JULEP

Into a 12 oz. Tom Collins glass put
4 Sprigs of Mint
1 Teaspoon Powdered Sugar
2½ oz. Old Mr. Boston Kentucky
    Bourbon Whiskey
Fill with shaved ice and stir gently until glass is frosted. Decorate with sprigs of mint. Serve with straws.

DIXIE WHISKEY COCKTAIL

½ Lump of Sugar
1 Dash Bitters
¼ Teaspoon Curacao
½ Teaspoon Old Mr. Boston
    Creme de Menthe (white)
2 oz. Old Mr. Boston Whiskey*
Shake well with cracked ice and strain into 3 oz. cocktail glass.

* Bourbon, Blended, Rye or Canadian.

D

DOUBLE STANDARD SOUR

Juice ½ Lemon or 1 Lime
½ Teaspoon Powdered Sugar
¾ oz. Old Mr. Boston Whiskey*
¾ oz. Old Mr. Boston Dry Gin
½ Teaspoon Raspberry Syrup or Grenadine
Shake well with cracked ice and strain into 6 oz. sour glass. Decorate with a half-slice of lemon and a cherry.

DREAM COCKTAIL

¾ oz. Curacao
1½ oz. Old Mr. Boston Five Star Brandy
¼ Teaspoon Old Mr. Boston Anisette
Shake well with cracked ice and strain into 3 oz. cocktail glass.

DRY MARTINI COCKTAIL

See *Special Martini Section* on pages 116 and 117.

DU BARRY COCKTAIL

1 Dash Bitters
¾ oz. Dry Vermouth
½ Teaspoon Absinthe Substitute
1½ oz. Old Mr. Boston Dry Gin
Stir well with cracked ice and strain into 3 oz. cocktail glass. Add slice of orange.

DUBONNET COCKTAIL

1½ oz. Dubonnet
¾ oz. Old Mr. Boston Dry Gin
1 Dash Orange Bitters *if desired.*
Stir well with cracked ice and strain into 3 oz. cocktail glass. Twist of lemon peel on top and drop in glass.

DUBONNET FIZZ

Juice ½ Orange
Juice ¼ Lemon
1 Teaspoon Old Mr. Boston Wild Cherry Flavored Brandy
2 oz. Dubonnet
Shake well with cracked ice and strain into 7 oz. highball glass. Fill with carbonated water and stir.

DUBONNET HIGHBALL

1 Cube of Ice
2 oz. Dubonnet
Fill 8 oz. highball glass with ginger ale or carbonated water. Add twist of lemon peel, if desired, and stir.

DUCHESS COCKTAIL

¾ oz. Dry Vermouth
¾ oz. Sweet Vermouth
¾ oz. Absinthe Substitute
Stir well with cracked ice and strain into 3 oz. cocktail glass.

DUKE COCKTAIL

½ oz. Triple Sec
1 Teaspoon Orange Juice
2 Teaspoons Lemon Juice
½ Teaspoon Maraschino
1 Egg
Shake well with cracked ice and strain into 8 oz. stem glass. Fill with Champagne and stir very gently.

* Bourbon, Blended, Rye or Canadian

East India Cocktail No. 1

1½ oz. Old Mr. Boston Five Star
   Brandy
½ Teaspoon Pineapple Juice
½ Teaspoon Curacao
1 Teaspoon Jamaica Rum
1 Dash Bitters
Shake well with cracked ice and strain into 3 oz. cocktail glass. Twist of lemon peel and add a cherry.

East India Cocktail No. 2

1¼ oz. Dry Vermouth
1¼ oz. Sherry Wine
1 Dash Orange Bitters
Stir well with cracked ice and strain into 3 oz. cocktail glass.

Eclipse Cocktail

1 oz. Old Mr. Boston Dry Gin
2 oz. Old Mr. Boston Sloe Gin
½ Teaspoon Lemon Juice
Put enough grenadine into 4 oz. cocktail glass to cover a ripe olive. Mix the above ingredients in ice and pour gently onto the grenadine so that they do not mix.

Eggnogs

See *Special Eggnog Section* on pages 114 and 115 and also Index on page 143 for complete list of Egg-nog recipes.

Egg Sour

1 Egg
1 Teaspoon Powdered Sugar
Juice ½ Lemon
2 oz. Old Mr. Boston Five Star
   Brandy
¼ Teaspoon Curacao
Shake well with cracked ice and strain into 8 oz. highball glass.

El Presidente Cocktail No. 1

Juice 1 Lime
1 Teaspoon Pineapple Juice
1 Teaspoon Grenadine
1½ oz. Old Mr. Boston Imported
   Rum
Shake well with cracked ice and strain into 3 oz. cocktail glass.

El Presidente Cocktail No. 2

¾ oz. Dry Vermouth
1½ oz. Old Mr. Boston Imported
   Rum
1 Dash Bitters
Stir well with cracked ice and strain into 3 oz. cocktail glass.

E

ELK'S OWN COCKTAIL

White of 1 Egg
1½ oz. Old Mr. Boston Whiskey*
¾ oz. Port Wine
Juice ¼ Lemon
1 Teaspoon Powdered Sugar
Add a strip of Pineapple. Shake well with cracked ice and strain into 4 oz. cocktail glass.

EMERALD ISLE COCKTAIL

2 oz. Old Mr. Boston Dry Gin
1 Teaspoon Old Mr. Boston
   Creme de Menthe (Green)
3 Dashes Bitters
Stir well with crackèd ice and strain into 3 oz. cocktail glass.

ENGLISH HIGHBALL

1 Cube of Ice
¾ oz. Old Mr. Boston Dry Gin
¾ oz. Old Mr. Boston Five Star
   Brandy
¾ oz. Sweet Vermouth
Fill 8 oz. highball glass with ginger ale or carbonated water. Add twist of lemon peel, if desired, and stir.

ENGLISH ROSE COCKTAIL

1¼ oz. Old Mr. Boston Dry Gin
¾ oz. Old Mr. Boston Apricot
   Flavored Brandy
¾ oz. Dry Vermouth
1 Teaspoon Grenadine
¼ Teaspoon Lemon Juice
Shake well with cracked ice and strain into 4 oz. cocktail glass. Frost rim of glass by rubbing with lemon and dipping in sugar. Serve with a cherry.

ETHEL DUFFY COCKTAIL

¾ oz. Old Mr. Boston Apricot
   Flavored Brandy
¾ oz. Old Mr. Boston Creme de
   Menthe (White)
¾ oz. Curacao
Shake well with cracked ice and strain into 3 oz. cocktail glass.

EVERYBODY'S IRISH COCKTAIL

1 Teaspoon Old Mr. Boston
   Creme de Menthe (Green)
1 Teaspoon Green Chartreuse
2 oz. Irish Whiskey
Stir well with cracked ice and strain into 3 oz. cocktail glass. Serve with green olive.

EYE-OPENER COCKTAIL

Yolk of 1 Egg
½ Teaspoon Powdered Sugar
1 Teaspoon Absinthe Substitute
1 Teaspoon Curacao
1 Teaspoon Old Mr. Boston
   Creme de Cacao
2 oz. Old Mr. Boston Imported
   Rum
Shake well with cracked ice and strain into 4 oz. cocktail glass.

* *Bourbon, Blended, Rye or Canadian*

FAIR AND WARMER COCKTAIL

¾ oz. Sweet Vermouth
1½ oz. Old Mr. Boston Imported Rum
½ Teaspoon Curacao
Stir well with cracked ice and strain into 3 oz. cocktail glass.

FAIRY BELLE COCKTAIL

White of 1 Egg
1 Teaspoon Grenadine
¾ oz. Old Mr. Boston Apricot Flavored Brandy
1½ oz. Old Mr. Boston Dry Gin
Shake well with cracked ice and strain into 4 oz. cocktail glass.

FALLEN ANGEL COCKTAIL

Juice of 1 Lemon or ½ Lime
1½ oz. Old Mr. Boston Dry Gin
1 Dash Bitters
½ Teaspoon Old Mr. Boston Creme de Menthe (white)
Shake well with cracked ice and strain into 3 oz. cocktail glass. Serve with a cherry.

FANCY BRANDY COCKTAIL

2 oz. Old Mr. Boston Five Star Brandy
1 Dash Bitters
¼ Teaspoon Curacao
¼ Teaspoon Powdered Sugar
Shake well with cracked ice and strain into 3 oz. cocktail glass. Twist of lemon peel and drop in glass.

FANCY GIN COCKTAIL

Same as FANCY BRANDY COCKTAIL *except substitute:* 2 oz. Old Mr. Boston Dry Gin

FANCY WHISKEY COCKTAIL

Same as FANCY BRANDY COCKTAIL *except substitute:* 2 oz. Old Mr. Boston Whiskey*

FANTASIO COCKTAIL

1 Teaspoon Old Mr. Boston Creme de Menthe (White)
1 Teaspoon Maraschino
1 oz. Old Mr. Boston Five Star Brandy
¾ oz. Dry Vermouth
Stir well with cracked ice and strain into 3 oz. cocktail glass.

36

* Bourbon, Blended, Rye or Canadian.

FARMER'S COCKTAIL

1 oz. Old Mr. Boston Dry Gin
½ oz. Dry Vermouth
½ oz. Sweet Vermouth
2 Dashes Bitters
Stir well with cracked ice and strain into 3 oz. cocktail glass.

FAVOURITE COCKTAIL

¾ oz. Old Mr. Boston Apricot Flavored Brandy
¾ oz. Dry Vermouth
¾ oz. Old Mr. Boston Dry Gin
¼ Teaspoon Lemon Juice
Shake well with cracked ice and strain into 3 oz. cocktail glass.

FIFTH AVENUE

⅓ oz. Old Mr. Boston Creme de Cacao
⅓ oz. Old Mr. Boston Apricot Flavored Brandy
⅓ oz. Sweet Cream
Pour carefully, in order given, into Pousse Café glass, so that each ingredient floats on preceding one.

FIFTY-FIFTY COCKTAIL

1¼ oz. Old Mr. Boston Dry Gin
1¼ oz. Dry Vermouth
Stir well with cracked ice and strain into 3 oz. cocktail glass.

FINE AND DANDY COCKTAIL

Juice of ¼ Lemon
½ oz. Triple Sec
1¼ oz. Old Mr. Boston Dry Gin
1 Dash Bitters
Shake well with cracked ice and strain into 3 oz. cocktail glass. Serve with a cherry.

FIREMAN'S SOUR

Juice 2 Limes
½ Teaspoon Powdered Sugar
½ oz. Grenadine
2 oz. Old Mr. Boston Imported Rum
Shake well with cracked ice and strain into Delmonico glass. Fill with carbonated water, if desired. Decorate with a half-slice of lemon and a cherry.

FISH HOUSE PUNCH

Juice of 1 Dozen Lemons
Add enough Powdered Sugar to sweeten. Place large block of ice in punch bowl and stir well. Then add:
1½ qts. Old Mr. Boston Five Star Brandy
1 pt. Old Mr. Boston Peach Flavored Brandy
1 pt. Old Mr. Boston Imported Rum
1 qt. Carbonated Water
Some prefer to add the strained contents of a pot of tea. Stir well and decorate with fruits in season. Serve in 4 oz. Punch glasses.

FIXES

See Index on page 143 for complete list of FIX recipes.

FIZZES

See Index on page 143 for complete list of FIZZ recipes.

FLAMINGO COCKTAIL
Juice of ½ Lime
½ oz. Old Mr. Boston Apricot Flavored Brandy
1¼ oz. Old Mr. Boston Dry Gin
1 Teaspoon Grenadine
Shake well with cracked ice and strain into 3 oz. cocktail glass.

FLIPS
See Index on page 143 for complete list of FLIP *recipes.*

FLORADORA COOLER
Into 12 oz. Tom Collins glass, put:
Juice 1 Lime
½ Teaspoon Powdered Sugar
½ oz. Raspberry Syrup or Grenadine
2 oz. Carbonated Water, and stir
Fill glass with cracked ice and add:
2 oz. Old Mr. Boston Dry Gin. *Fill with carbonated water or ginger ale and stir again.*

FLYING GRASSHOPPER COCKTAIL
¾ oz. Old Mr. Boston Creme de Menthe (green)
¾ oz. Old Mr. Boston Creme de Cacao (white)
¾ oz. Old Mr. Boston Vodka
Stir well with cracked ice and strain into 3 oz. cocktail glass.

FLYING SCOTCHMAN COCKTAIL
1 oz. Sweet Vermouth
1 oz. Old Mr. Boston Scotch Whisky
1 Dash Bitters
¼ Teaspoon Simple Syrup
Stir well with cracked ice and strain into 3 oz. cocktail glass.

FOG HORN
1 Cube of Ice
Juice of ½ Lime
1½ oz. Old Mr. Boston Dry Gin
Fill 8 oz. highball glass with ginger ale and stir. Leave lime in glass.

FOX RIVER COCKTAIL
½ oz. Old Mr. Boston Creme de Cacao
2 oz. Old Mr. Boston Whiskey*
4 Dashes Bitters
Stir well with cracked ice and strain into 3 oz. cocktail glass.

FRANKENJACK COCKTAIL
1 oz. Old Mr. Boston Dry Gin
¾ oz. Dry Vermouth
½ oz. Old Mr. Boston Apricot Flavored Brandy
1 Teaspoon Triple Sec
Stir well with cracked ice and strain into 3 oz. cocktail glass. Serve with a cherry.

FRENCH "75"
Juice of 1 Lemon
2 Teaspoons Powdered Sugar
Stir well in 12 oz. Tom Collins glass. Then add 1 Cube of Ice, 2 oz. Old Mr. Boston Dry Gin and fill with Champagne and stir gently. Decorate with slice of lemon, orange and a cherry. Serve with straws.

* *Bourbon, Blended, Rye or Canadian*

Frisco Sour
Juice ¼ Lemon
Juice ½ Lime
½ oz. Benedictine
2 oz. Old Mr. Boston Whiskey*
Shake well with cracked ice and strain into 6 oz. sour glass. Decorate with slices of lemon and lime.

Froth Blower Cocktail
White of 1 Egg
1 Teaspoon Grenadine
2 oz. Old Mr. Boston Dry Gin
Shake well with cracked ice and strain into 4 oz. cocktail glass.

Froupe Cocktail
1¼ oz. Sweet Vermouth
1¼ oz. Old Mr. Boston Five Star Brandy
1 Teaspoon Benedictine
Stir well with cracked ice and strain into 3 oz. cocktail glass.

Frozen Daiquiri Cocktail
Juice 1 Lime
1 Teaspoon Powdered Sugar
2 oz. Old Mr. Boston Imported Rum
Agitate in electric mixer filled with shaved ice for about 2 minutes. Strain through coarse meshed strainer into 6 oz. Champagne glass.

General Harrison's Eggnog
1 Egg
1 Teaspoon Powdered Sugar
Shake well with cracked ice and strain into 12 oz. Tom Collins glass. Fill glass with Claret or sweet cider and stir gently. Grate nutmeg on top.

Gibson Cocktail
See *Special Martini Section* on pages 116 and 117.

Gilroy Cocktail
Juice of ¼ Lemon
½ oz. Dry Vermouth
¾ oz. Old Mr. Boston Wild Cherry Flavored Brandy
¾ oz. Old Mr. Boston Dry Gin
1 Dash Orange Bitters
Shake well with cracked ice and strain into 3 oz. cocktail glass.

39

* Bourbon, Blended, Rye or Canadian.

G

GIMLET COCKTAIL

Juice 1 Lime
1 Teaspoon Powdered Sugar
1½ oz. Old Mr. Boston Dry Gin
Shake well with cracked ice and strain into 4 oz. cocktail glass.

GIN AND BITTERS

Put ½ teaspoon bitters into 3 oz. cocktail glass and revolve glass until it is entirely coated with the bitters. Then fill with Old Mr. Boston Dry Gin. No ice is used in this drink.

GIN AND IT (English)

2 oz. Old Mr. Boston Dry Gin
1 oz. Sweet Vermouth
Stir. No ice is used in this drink. Serve in 3 oz. cocktail glass.

GIN AND TONIC

2 oz. Old Mr. Boston Dry Gin
Cube of Ice
Fill glass with quinine water and stir. Use 12 oz. Tom Collins glass.

GIN BUCK

1 Cube of Ice
Juice of ½ Lemon
1½ oz. Old Mr. Boston Dry Gin
Fill 8 oz. highball glass with ginger ale and stir.

GIN COBBLER

Dissolve: 1 Teaspoon Powdered Sugar *in* 2 oz. Carbonated Water, *then* fill *10 oz. goblet with shaved ice, and add*
2 oz. Old Mr. Boston Dry Gin
Stir well and decorate with fruits in season. Serve with straws.

GIN COCKTAIL

2 oz. Old Mr. Boston Dry Gin
2 Dashes Bitters
Stir well with cracked ice and strain into 3 oz. cocktail glass. Serve with a twist of lemon peel.

GIN COOLER

Into 12 oz. Tom Collins glass, put:
½ Teaspoon Powdered Sugar
2 oz. Carbonated Water, and stir
Fill glass with cracked ice and add:
2 oz. Old Mr. Boston Dry Gin
Fill with carbonated water or ginger ale and stir again. Insert spiral of orange or lemon peel (or both) and dangle end over rim of glass.

GIN DAISY

Juice of ½ Lemon
½ Teaspoon Powdered Sugar
1 Teaspoon Raspberry Syrup or Grenadine
2 oz. Old Mr. Boston Dry Gin
Shake well with cracked ice and strain into stein or 8 oz. metal cup. Add cube of ice and decorate with fruit.

GIN FIX

Juice ½ Lemon
1 Teaspoon Powdered Sugar
1 Teaspoon Water
Stir and fill glass with shaved ice. Add
2½ oz. Old Mr. Boston Dry Gin
Use 8 oz. highball glass. Stir well. Add slice of lemon. Serve with straws.

G

GIN FIZZ

uice ½ Lemon
Teaspoon Powdered Sugar
oz. Old Mr. Boston Dry Gin
Shake well with cracked ice and strain into 7 oz. highball glass. Fill with carbonated water and stir.

GIN HIGHBALL

Cube of Ice
oz. Old Mr. Boston Dry Gin
Fill 8 oz. highball glass with ginger le or carbonated water. Add twist f lemon peel, if desired, and stir.

GIN MILK PUNCH

Teaspoon Powdered Sugar
oz. Old Mr. Boston Dry Gin
½ pt. Milk
Shake well with cracked ice, strain nto 12 oz. Tom Collins glass and rate nutmeg on top.

GIN RICKEY

Cube of Ice
uice ½ Lime
½ oz. Old Mr. Boston Dry Gin
Fill 8 oz. highball glass with carbonted water and stir. Leave lime in lass.

GIN SANGAREE

Dissolve ½ teaspoon powdered sugar n 1 teaspoon of water. Add
oz. Old Mr. Boston Dry Gin
cubes of ice.
erve in 8 oz. highball glass. Fill alance with soda water. Stir, leav-ng enough room on which to float a ablespoon of Port Wine. Sprinkle ightly with nutmeg.

GIN SLING

Dissolve 1 teaspoon powdered sugar in 1 teaspoon water and juice ½ lemon.
2 oz. Old Mr. Boston Dry Gin
2 Cubes of Ice
Serve in Old Fashioned cocktail glass and stir. Twist of orange peel and drop in glass.

GIN SMASH

Muddle 1 Lump of Sugar with
1 oz. Carbonated Water and
4 Sprigs of Green Mint
Add 2 oz. Old Mr. Boston Dry Gin and a cube of ice. Stir and decorate with a slice of orange and a cherry. Twist lemon peel on top. Use Old Fashioned cocktail glass.

GIN SOUR

Juice of ½ Lemon
½ Teaspoon Powdered Sugar
2 oz. Old Mr. Boston Dry Gin
Shake well with cracked ice and strain into 6 oz. sour glass. Decorate with a half-slice of lemon and a cherry.

G

GIN SQUIRT

1½ oz. Old Mr. Boston Dry Gin
1 Tablespoon Powdered Sugar
1 Teaspoon Raspberry Syrup or
   Grenadine
*Stir well with cracked ice and strain
into 8 oz. highball glass; fill with
carbonated water and stir. Decorate
with cubes of pineapple and strawberries.*

GIN SWIZZLE

Into 12 oz. Tom Collins glass put:
Juice 1 Lime
1 Teaspoon Powdered Sugar
2 oz. Carbonated Water
*Fill glass with shaved ice and stir
thoroughly with swizzle stick. Then
add:*
2 Dashes Bitters
2 oz. Old Mr. Boston Dry Gin
*Fill with carbonated water and serve
with swizzle stick in glass, allowing
individual to do final stirring.*

GIN TODDY

Use Old Fashioned cocktail glass.
½ Teaspoon Powdered Sugar
2 Teaspoons Water *and stir.*
2 oz. Old Mr. Boston Dry Gin
1 Lump of Ice
Stir well and twist lemon peel on top.

GIN TODDY (Hot)

*Put lump of sugar into hot whiskey
glass and fill two-thirds with boiling
water. Add 2 oz. Old Mr. Boston
Dry Gin. Stir and decorate with
slice of lemon. Grate nutmeg on top.*

GLÖGG

Pour following into kettle:
2 ⅘ Qts. Wine (Port, Sherry,
Claret, Burgundy or Madeira)
Insert cheesecloth bag containing:
   2 oz. Dried Orange Peel
   2 oz. Cinnamon Sticks
   20 Cardamon Seeds
   25 Cloves
*and boil slowly for 15 minutes, stir-
ring occasionally. Add 1 lb. each
blanched almonds and seedless raisins and continue to boil for additional 15 minutes. Remove kettle
from stove and place wire grill containing 1 lb. lump sugar over
opening. Pour ⅓ qt. of Old Mr.
Boston Five Star Brandy over sugar
making sure to saturate all of it.
Then light sugar with match and let
it flame. After sugar has melted replace kettle cover to extinguish flame.
Stir again and remove spice bag.
Serve hot in punch cups with a few
almonds and raisins.*

GOLDEN SLIPPER COCKTAIL

¾ oz. Yellow Chartreuse
2 oz. Old Mr. Boston Apricot Flavored Brandy
*Stir well with cracked ice and strain
into 4 oz. cocktail glass. Float yolk of
egg on top.*

GOLF COCKTAIL

1½ oz. Old Mr. Boston Dry Gin
¾ oz. Dry Vermouth
2 Dashes Bitters
*Stir well with cracked ice and strain
into 3 oz. cocktail glass.*

G

Grand Royal Fizz

Juice ¼ Orange
Juice ½ Lemon
1 Teaspoon Powdered Sugar
2 oz. Old Mr. Boston Dry Gin
½ Teaspoon Maraschino
2 Teaspoons Sweet Cream
Shake well with cracked ice and strain into 8 oz. highball glass. Fill with carbonated water and stir.

Grapefruit Cocktail

1 oz. Grapefruit Juice
1 oz. Old Mr. Boston Dry Gin
1 Teaspoon Maraschino
Shake well with cracked ice and strain into 3 oz. cocktail glass. Serve with a cherry.

Grasshopper Cocktail

¾ oz. Old Mr. Boston Creme de Menthe (green)
¾ oz. Old Mr. Boston Creme de Cacao (white)
¾ oz. Light Sweet Cream
Shake well with cracked ice and strain into 3 oz. cocktail glass.

Green Dragon Cocktail

Juice of ¼ Lemon
½ oz. Old Mr. Boston Kummel
½ oz. Old Mr. Boston Creme de Menthe (Green)
1½ oz. Old Mr. Boston Dry Gin
4 Dashes Orange Bitters
Shake well with cracked ice and strain into 4 oz. cocktail glass.

Green Fizz

1 Teaspoon Powdered Sugar
White 1 Egg
Juice ½ Lemon
2 oz. Old Mr. Boston Dry Gin
1 Teaspoon Old Mr. Boston Creme de Menthe (Green)
Shake well with cracked ice and strain into 8 oz. highball glass. Fill with carbonated water and stir.

Green Swizzle

Make same as Gin Swizzle *(see page 43), and add 1 tablespoon Old Mr. Boston Green Creme de Menthe. If desired, rum, brandy or whiskey may be substituted for the gin.*

Grenadine Rickey

1 Cube of Ice
Juice ½ Lime
1½ oz. Grenadine
Fill 8 oz. highball glass with carbonated water and stir. Leave lime in glass.

Gypsy Cocktail

1¼ oz. Sweet Vermouth
1¼ oz. Old Mr. Boston Dry Gin
Stir well with cracked ice and strain into 3 oz. cocktail glass. Serve with a cherry.

HARLEM COCKTAIL
¾ oz. Pineapple Juice
1½ oz. Old Mr. Boston Dry Gin
½ Teaspoon Maraschino
2 Cubes of Pineapple
Shake well with cracked ice and strain into 3 oz. cocktail glass.

HARRY LAUDER COCKTAIL
1¼ oz. Old Mr. Boston Scotch Whisky
1¼ oz. Sweet Vermouth
½ Teaspoon Simple Syrup
Stir well with cracked ice and strain into 3 oz. cocktail glass.

HARVARD COCKTAIL
1½ oz. Old Mr. Boston Five Star Brandy
¾ oz. Sweet Vermouth
1 Dash Bitters
1 Teaspoon Grenadine
2 Teaspoons Lemon Juice
Shake well with cracked ice and strain into 3 oz. cocktail glass.

HARVARD COOLER
Into 12 oz. Tom Collins glass put:
½ Teaspoon Powdered Sugar
2 oz. Carbonated Water
Stir. Then fill glass with cracked ice and add:
2 oz. Apple Brandy
Fill with carbonated water or ginger ale and stir again. Insert spiral of orange or lemon peel (or both) and dangle end over rim of glass.

HASTY COCKTAIL
¾ oz. Dry Vermouth
1½ oz. Old Mr. Boston Dry Gin
¼ Teaspoon Absinthe Substitute
1 Teaspoon Grenadine
Stir well with cracked ice and strain into 3 oz. cocktail glass.

HAVANA COCKTAIL
1¼ oz. Pineapple Juice
½ Teaspoon Lemon Juice
¾ oz. Old Mr. Boston Imported Rum
Shake well with cracked ice and strain into 3 oz. cocktail glass.

HAWAIIAN COCKTAIL
2 oz. Old Mr. Boston Dry Gin
½ oz. Pineapple Juice
½ oz. Curacao
Shake well with cracked ice and strain into 4 oz. cocktail glass.

HEADLESS HORSEMAN
Into 12 oz. Tom Collins glass, put:
2 oz. Old Mr. Boston Vodka
3 Dashes Bitters
Add several cubes of ice, fill with dry ginger ale and stir. Decorate with slice of orange.

HIGHBALLS
See Index on page 144 for complete list of HIGHBALL *recipes.*

HIGHLAND COOLER
Into 12 oz. Tom Collins glass, put:
½ Teaspoon Powdered Sugar
2 oz. Carbonated Water, and stir.
Fill glass with cracked ice and add:
2 oz. Old Mr. Boston Scotch Whisky
Fill with carbonated water or ginger ale and stir again. Insert spiral of orange or lemon peel (or both) and dangle end over rim of glass.

HIGHLAND FLING COCKTAIL
¾ oz. Sweet Vermouth
1½ oz. Old Mr. Boston Scotch Whisky
2 Dashes Orange Bitters
Stir well with cracked ice and strain into 3 oz. cocktail glass. Serve with an olive.

OLD Mr. BOSTON BRAND
Rocking Chair
KENTUCKY
WHISKEY
A Blend

BLENDED AND BOTTLED BY MR. BOSTON DISTILLER INC. BOSTON

◄ Rocking Chair Kentucky Whiskey—A Blend
80 Proof 72½% Grain Neutral Spirits

H

Hill Billy Highball

1 Cube of Ice
2 ozs. Georgia Moon Corn Whiskey
Fill 8 oz. highball glass with Mountain Dew.
Then add twist of lemon peel if desired and stir.

Hoffman House Cocktail

¾ oz. Dry Vermouth
1½ oz. Old Mr. Boston Dry Gin
2 Dashes Orange Bitters
Stir well with cracked ice and strain into 3 oz. cocktail glass. Serve with an olive.

Hole-in-One Cocktail

1½ oz. Old Mr. Boston Scotch
  Whisky
¾ oz. Dry Vermouth
¼ Teaspoon Lemon Juice
1 Dash Orange Bitters
Shake well with cracked ice and strain into 3 oz. cocktail glass.

Homestead Cocktail

1½ oz. Old Mr. Boston Dry Gin
¾ oz. Sweet Vermouth
Stir well with cracked ice and strain into 3 oz. cocktail glass and serve with slice of orange.

Honeymoon Cocktail

¾ oz. Benedictine
¾ oz. Apple Brandy
Juice of ½ Lemon
1 Teaspoon Curacao
Shake well with cracked ice and strain into 3 oz. cocktail glass.

Honolulu Cocktail No. 1

1 Dash Bitters
¼ Teaspoon Orange Juice
¼ Teaspoon Pineapple Juice
¼ Teaspoon Lemon Juice
½ Teaspoon Powdered Sugar
1½ oz. Old Mr. Boston Dry Gin
Shake well with cracked ice and strain into 3 oz. cocktail glass.

Honolulu Cocktail No. 2

¾ oz. Old Mr. Boston Dry Gin
¾ oz. Maraschino
¾ oz. Benedictine
Stir well with cracked ice and strain into 3 oz. cocktail glass.

Hoot Mon Cocktail

¾ oz. Sweet Vermouth
1½ oz. Old Mr. Boston Scotch
  Whisky
1 Teaspoon Benedictine
Stir well with cracked ice and strain into 3 oz. cocktail glass. Twist of lemon peel and drop in glass.

Hop Toad Cocktail

Juice ½ Lime
¾ oz. Old Mr. Boston Apricot Flavored Brandy
¾ oz. Old Mr. Boston Imported Rum
Stir well with cracked ice and strain into 3 oz. cocktail glass.

Horses Neck (With a Kick)

Peel rind of whole lemon in spiral fashion and put in 12 oz. Tom Collins glass with one end hanging over the rim. Fill glass with ice cubes. Add 2 oz. Old Mr. Boston Whiskey.* Then fill with ginger ale and stir well.

47

* *Bourbon, Blended, Rye or Canadian.*

Hot Brandy Flip

1 Egg
1 Teaspoon Powdered Sugar
1½ oz. Old Mr. Boston Five Star Brandy
Beat egg, sugar and brandy and pour into Tom & Jerry Mug and fill with hot milk. Grate nutmeg on top.

Hot Brick Toddy

Into hot whiskey glass, put:
1 Teaspoon Butter
1 Teaspoon Powdered Sugar
3 Pinches Cinnamon
1 oz. Hot Water
Dissolve thoroughly. Then add:
1½ oz. Old Mr. Boston Whiskey*
Fill with boiling water and stir.

Hot Buttered Rum

Put lump of sugar into hot whiskey glass and fill two-thirds with boiling water. Add square of butter and 2 oz. Old Mr. Boston Imported Rum. Stir and grate nutmeg on top.

Hot Buttered Wine

For each serving—heat ½ cup Muscatel Wine. Add ¼ cup water just to simmering; do not boil. Preheat mug or cup with boiling water. Pour heated wine mixture into mug and add 1 teaspoon butter and 2 teaspoons maple syrup. Stir well and sprinkle nutmeg on top. Serve at once.

Hot Drinks

See Index on page 144 for complete list of Hot Drink Recipes.

Hot Springs Cocktail

1½ oz. Dry White Wine
½ oz. Pineapple Juice
½ Teaspoon Maraschino
1 Dash Orange Bitters
Shake well with cracked ice and strain into 3 oz. cocktail glass.

Hotel Plaza Cocktail

¾ oz. Sweet Vermouth
¾ oz. Dry Vermouth
¾ oz. Old Mr. Boston Dry Gin
Crush 1 Slice of Pineapple
Stir well with cracked ice and strain into 3 oz. cocktail glass.

H. P. W. Cocktail

¼ oz. Dry Vermouth
¼ oz. Sweet Vermouth
1½ oz. Old Mr. Boston Dry Gin
Stir well with cracked ice and strain into 3 oz. cocktail glass. Twist of orange peel and drop in glass.

Hula-Hula Cocktail

¾ oz. Orange Juice
1½ oz. Old Mr. Boston Dry Gin
¼ Teaspoon Powdered Sugar
Shake well with cracked ice and strain into 3 oz. cocktail glass.

Huntsman Cocktail

1½ oz. Old Mr. Boston Vodka
½ oz. Jamaica Rum
Juice of ½ Lime
Powdered sugar to taste
Shake well with cracked ice and strain into 3 oz. cocktail glass.

* *Bourbon, Blended, Rye or Canadian.*

ICE CREAM FLIP

Egg
oz. Maraschino
oz. Curacao
Small Scoop Vanilla Ice Cream
*Shake well with cracked ice and
strain into 5 oz. flip glass. Grate a
little nutmeg on top.*

IDEAL COCKTAIL

oz. Dry Vermouth
oz. Old Mr. Boston Dry Gin
Teaspoon Maraschino
Teaspoon Grapefruit or Lemon
   Juice
*Shake well with cracked ice and
strain into 3 oz. cocktail glass. Serve
with a cherry.*

IMPERIAL COCKTAIL

¼ oz. Dry Vermouth
¼ oz. Old Mr. Boston Dry Gin
Teaspoon Maraschino
Dash Bitters
*Stir well with cracked ice and strain
into 3 oz. cocktail glass. Serve with a
cherry.*

IMPERIAL FIZZ

Juice of ½ Lemon
½ oz. Old Mr. Boston Imported
   Rum
1½ oz. Old Mr. Boston Whiskey*
1 Teaspoon Powdered Sugar
*Shake well with cracked ice and
strain into 7 oz. highball glass. Fill
with carbonated water and stir.*

INCOME TAX COCKTAIL

¼ oz. Dry Vermouth
¼ oz. Sweet Vermouth
1 oz. Old Mr. Boston Dry Gin
1 Dash Bitters
Juice of ¼ Orange
*Shake well with cracked ice and
strain into 3 oz. cocktail glass.*

IRISH COFFEE

*Into a pre-warmed 8 oz. stemmed
glass (or coffee cup), pour 1½ oz.
Irish Whiskey. Add 1 or 2 teaspoons
sugar and fill to within ½ inch of
top with strong, very hot black coffee.
Stir to dissolve sugar. Float to brim
with chilled whipped cream. Do not
stir. Drink through floating cream.*

19

Bourbon, Blended, Rye or Canadian.

IRISH RICKEY

1 Cube of Ice
Juice of ½ Lime
1½ oz. Irish Whiskey
Fill 8 oz. highball glass with carbonated water and stir. Leave lime in glass.

IRISH SHILLELAGH

Juice ½ Lemon
1 Teaspoon Powdered Sugar
1½ oz. Irish Whiskey
½ oz. Old Mr. Boston Sloe Gin
½ oz. Old Mr. Boston Imported
   Rum
2 Slices of Peach
Shake well with cracked ice and strain into 5 oz. punch glass. Decorate with fresh raspberries, strawberries and a cherry.

IRISH WHISKEY COCKTAIL

½ Teaspoon Curacao
½ Teaspoon Absinthe Substitute
¼ Teaspoon Maraschino
1 Dash Bitters
2 oz. Irish Whiskey
Stir well with cracked ice and strain into 3 oz. cocktail glass. Serve with an olive.

IRISH WHISKEY HIGHBALL

1 Cube of Ice
2 oz. Irish Whiskey
Fill 8 oz. highball glass with ginger ale or carbonated water. Add twist of lemon peel, if desired, and stir.

JACK-IN-THE-BOX COCKTAIL

1 oz. Apple Brandy
1 oz. Pineapple Juice
Dash of Bitters
Shake well with cracked ice and strain into 3 oz. cocktail glass.

JACK ROSE COCKTAIL

1½ oz. Apple Brandy
Juice ½ Lime
1 Teaspoon Grenadine
Shake well with cracked ice and strain into 3 oz. cocktail glass.

JAMAICA GLOW COCKTAIL

1 oz. Old Mr. Boston Dry Gin
½ oz. Claret
½ oz. Orange Juice
1 Teaspoon Jamaica Rum
Shake well with cracked ice and strain into 3 oz. cocktail glass.

JAMAICA GRANITO

Small scoop of either Lemon or
    Orange Sherbet
1½ oz. Old Mr. Boston Five Star
    Brandy
1 oz. Curacao
*Use 12 oz. Tom Collins glass and fill
balance with carbonated water and
stir. Grate nutmeg on top.*

JAPANESE FIZZ

Juice ½ Lemon
1 Teaspoon Powdered Sugar
1½ oz. Old Mr. Boston Whiskey*
½ oz. Port Wine
White 1 Egg
*Shake well with cracked ice and
strain into 8 oz. highball glass. Fill
with carbonated water and stir.
Serve with slice of pineapple.*

JERSEY LIGHTNING COCKTAIL

1½ oz. Apple Brandy
½ oz. Sweet Vermouth
Juice 1 Lime
*Shake well with cracked ice and
strain into 3 oz. cocktail glass.*

* *Bourbon, Blended, Rye or Canadian.*

J

Jewel Cocktail

¾ oz. Green Chartreuse
¾ oz. Sweet Vermouth
¾ oz. Old Mr. Boston Dry Gin
1 Dash Orange Bitters
Stir well with cracked ice and strain into 3 oz. cocktail glass. Serve with a cherry.

Jeyplak Cocktail

1½ oz. Old Mr. Boston Dry Gin
¾ oz. Sweet Vermouth
¼ Teaspoon Absinthe Substitute
Stir well with cracked ice and strain into 3 oz. cocktail glass. Serve with a cherry.

Jockey Club Cocktail

1 Dash Bitters
¼ Teaspoon Old Mr. Boston Creme de Cacao
Juice of ¼ Lemon
1½ oz. Old Mr. Boston Dry Gin
Shake well with cracked ice and strain into 3 oz. cocktail glass.

John Collins

Juice ½ Lemon
1 Teaspoon Powdered Sugar
2 oz. Holland Gin
Shake well with cracked ice and strain into 12 oz. Tom Collins glass. Add several cubes of ice, fill with carbonated water and stir. Decorate with slice of orange, lemon and a cherry. Serve with straws.

Johnnie Cocktail

¾ oz. Curacao
1½ oz. Old Mr. Boston Sloe Gin
1 Teaspoon Old Mr. Boston Anisette
Stir well with cracked ice and strain into 3 oz. cocktail glass.

Journalist Cocktail

¼ oz. Dry Vermouth
¼ oz. Sweet Vermouth
1½ oz. Old Mr. Boston Dry Gin
½ Teaspoon Lemon Juice
½ Teaspoon Curacao
1 Dash Bitters
Shake well with cracked ice and strain into 3 oz. cocktail glass.

Judge Jr. Cocktail

¾ oz. Old Mr. Boston Dry Gin
¾ oz. Old Mr. Boston Imported Rum
Juice of ¼ Lemon
½ Teaspoon Powdered Sugar
¼ Teaspoon Grenadine
Shake well with cracked ice and strain into 3 oz. cocktail glass.

Judgette Cocktail

¾ oz. Old Mr. Boston Peach Flavored Brandy
¾ oz. Old Mr. Boston Dry Gin
¾ oz. Dry Vermouth
Juice of ¼ Lime
Shake well with cracked ice and strain into 3 oz. cocktail glass. Serve with a cherry.

Juleps

See Index on page 144 for complete list of Julep recipes.

K

KANGAROO COCKTAIL
1½ oz. Old Mr. Boston Vodka
¾ oz. Dry Vermouth
Stir well with cracked ice and strain into 3 oz. cocktail glass. Serve with twist of lemon peel.

K. C. B. COCKTAIL
½ oz. Old Mr. Boston Kummel
1½ oz. Old Mr. Boston Dry Gin
¼ Teaspoon Old Mr. Boston Apricot Flavored Brandy
¼ Teaspoon Lemon Juice
Shake well with cracked ice and strain into 3 oz. cocktail glass. Add twist of lemon peel and drop in glass.

KENTUCKY COCKTAIL
1½ oz. Pineapple Juice
¾ oz. Old Mr. Boston Kentucky Bourbon Whiskey
Shake well with cracked ice and strain into 3 oz. cocktail glass.

KENTUCKY COLONEL COCKTAIL
½ oz. Benedictine
1½ oz. Old Mr. Boston Kentucky Bourbon Whiskey
Twist of Lemon Peel
Stir well with cracked ice and strain into a 3 oz. cocktail glass.

KING COLE COCKTAIL
1 Slice of Orange
1 Slice of Pineapple
½ Teaspoon Powdered Sugar
Muddle well in Old Fashioned cocktail glass and add:
2 oz. Old Mr. Boston Whiskey*
1 Cube of Ice
Stir well.

53

* *Bourbon, Blended, Rye or Canadian.*

KISS-IN-THE-DARK COCKTAIL

¾ oz. Old Mr. Boston Dry Gin
¾ oz. Old Mr. Boston Wild Cherry
   Flavored Brandy
¾ oz. Dry Vermouth
*Stir well with cracked ice and strain
into 3 oz. cocktail glass.*

KLONDIKE COOLER

Into 12 oz. Tom Collins glass, put:
½ Teaspoon Powdered Sugar
2 oz. Carbonated Water
*Stir and fill glass with cracked ice
and add:*
2 oz. Old Mr. Boston Whiskey*
*Fill with carbonated water or gin-
ger ale and stir again. Insert spiral
of orange or lemon peel (or both) and
dangle end over rim of glass.*

KNICKERBOCKER COCKTAIL

¼ Teaspoon Sweet Vermouth
¼ oz. Dry Vermouth
1½ oz. Old Mr. Boston Dry Gin
*Stir well with cracked ice, strain into
3 oz. glass. Add twist of lemon peel
and drop in glass.*

KNICKERBOCKER SPECIAL COCKTAIL

1 Teaspoon Raspberry Syrup
1 Teaspoon Lemon Juice
1 Teaspoon Orange Juice
2 oz. Old Mr. Boston Imported
   Rum
½ Teaspoon Curacao
*Shake well with cracked ice and
strain into 4 oz. cocktail glass. Decorate with small slice of pineapple.*

KNOCK-OUT COCKTAIL

½ oz. Absinthe Substitute
¾ oz. Old Mr. Boston Dry Gin
¾ oz. Dry Vermouth
1 Teaspoon Old Mr. Boston
   Creme de Menthe (white)
*Stir well with cracked ice and strain
into 3 oz. cocktail glass. Serve with a
cherry.*

KRETCHMA COCKTAIL

1 oz. Old Mr. Boston Vodka
1 oz. Old Mr. Boston Creme de
   Cacao
½ oz. Lemon Juice
1 Dash Grenadine
*Shake well with cracked ice and
strain into 3 oz. cocktail glass.*

KUP'S INDISPENSABLE COCKTAIL

½ oz. Sweet Vermouth
½ oz. Dry Vermouth
1¼ oz. Old Mr. Boston Dry Gin
1 Dash Bitters
*Stir well with cracked ice and strain
into 3 oz. cocktail glass.*

Bourbon, Blended, Rye or Canadian.

80 Proof 100% Grain Neutral Spirits

L

LADIES' COCKTAIL

1¾ oz. Old Mr. Boston Whiskey*
½ Teaspoon Absinthe Substitute
½ Teaspoon Old Mr. Boston
 Anisette
2 Dashes Bitters
*Stir well with cracked ice and strain
into 3 oz. cocktail glass. Serve with a
piece of pineapple on top.*

LADY LOVE FIZZ

1 Teaspoon Powdered Sugar
Juice of ½ Lemon
White of 1 Egg
2 oz. Old Mr. Boston Dry Gin
2 Teaspoons Sweet Cream
*Shake well with cracked ice and
strain into 8 oz. highball glass. Fill
with carbonated water and stir.*

LASKY COCKTAIL

¾ oz. Grape Juice
¾ oz. Swedish Punch
¾ oz. Old Mr. Boston Dry Gin
*Shake well with cracked ice and
strain into 3 oz. cocktail glass.*

LAWHILL COCKTAIL

¾ oz. Dry Vermouth
1½ oz. Old Mr. Boston Whiskey*
¼ Teaspoon Absinthe Substitute
¼ Teaspoon Maraschino
1 Dash Bitters
*Stir well with cracked ice and strain
into 3 oz. cocktail glass.*

LEAP FROG HIGHBALL

Juice ½ Lemon
2 oz. Old Mr. Boston Dry Gin
1 Cube of Ice
*Fill 8 oz. highball glass with ginger
ale and stir gently.*

LEAP YEAR COCKTAIL

1¼ oz. Old Mr. Boston Dry Gin
½ oz. Old Mr. Boston Orange
 Flavored Gin
½ oz. Sweet Vermouth
¼ Teaspoon Lemon Juice
*Shake well with cracked ice and
strain into 3 oz. cocktail glass.*

56

LEAVE IT TO ME COCKTAIL No. 1

/2 oz. Old Mr. Boston Apricot
　Flavored Brandy
/2 oz. Dry Vermouth
1 oz. Old Mr. Boston Dry Gin
/4 Teaspoon Lemon Juice
/4 Teaspoon Grenadine
*Shake well with cracked ice and
strain into 3 oz. cocktail glass.*

LEAVE IT TO ME COCKTAIL No. 2

Teaspoon Raspberry Syrup
Teaspoon Lemon Juice
/4 Teaspoon Maraschino
½ oz. Old Mr. Boston Dry Gin
*Stir well with cracked ice and strain
into 3 oz. cocktail glass.*

LEMON SQUASH

Lemon, peeled and quartered
Teaspoons Powdered Sugar
*Muddle well in 12 oz. Tom Collins
glass until juice is well extracted.
Then fill glass with cracked ice. Add
carbonated water and stir. Decorate
with fruits.*

LEMONADE (Carbonated)

Teaspoons Powdered Sugar
Juice 1 Lemon
*Stir. Then fill 12 oz. Tom Collins
glass with shaved ice. Add enough
carbonated water to fill glass and
stir. Decorate with slice of orange,
lemon and a cherry. Serve with
straws.*

LEMONADE (Claret)

2 Teaspoons Powdered Sugar
Juice 1 Lemon
*Stir. Then fill 12 oz. Tom Collins
glass with shaved ice. Add enough
water to fill glass, leaving room to
float 2 oz. Claret. Decorate with slice
of orange, lemon and a cherry. Serve
with straws.*

LEMONADE (Egg)

Juice 1 Lemon
2 Teaspoons Powdered Sugar
1 Whole Egg
*Shake well and strain into 12 oz.
Tom Collins glass filled with shaved
ice. Add enough water to fill glass.
Serve with straws.*

LEMONADE (Fruit)

Juice 1 Lemon
2 Teaspoons Powdered Sugar
1 oz. Raspberry Syrup
*Stir. Then fill 12 oz. Tom Collins
glass with shaved ice. Add enough
water to fill glass and stir. Decorate
with a slice of orange, lemon and a
cherry. Serve with straws.*

LEMONADE (Golden)

Juice 1 Lemon
2 Teaspoons Powdered Sugar
Yolk of 1 Egg
6 oz. Water
*Shake well with cracked ice and
strain into 12 oz. Tom Collins glass.
Decorate with a slice of orange, lemon
and a cherry.*

L

LEMONADE (Modern)

2 Teaspoons Powdered Sugar
1½ oz. Sherry Wine
1 oz. Old Mr. Boston Sloe Gin
*Cut lemon in quarters and muddle
well with sugar. Add sherry and sloe
gin. Shake well with cracked ice and
strain into 12 oz. Tom Collins glass.
Fill glass with carbonated water.*

LEMONADE (Plain)

2 Teaspoons Powdered Sugar
Juice 1 Lemon
*Stir. Then fill 12 oz. Tom Collins
glass with shaved ice. Add enough
water to fill glass and stir well. Decorate with slice of orange, lemon and
a cherry.*

LIBERTY COCKTAIL

¾ oz. Old Mr. Boston Imported
   Rum
1½ oz. Apple Brandy
¼ Teaspoon Simple Syrup
*Stir well with cracked ice and strain
into 3 oz. cocktail glass.*

LIMEADE

Juice 3 Limes
3 Teaspoons Powdered Sugar
*Fill 12 oz. Tom Collins glass with
shaved ice. Add enough water to fill
glass. Stir well and drop lime in
glass. Add a cherry. Serve with
straws.*

LINSTEAD COCKTAIL

1 oz. Old Mr. Boston Whiskey*
1 oz. Pineapple Juice
½ Teaspoon Powdered Sugar
¼ Teaspoon Absinthe Substitute
¼ Teaspoon Lemon Juice
*Shake well with cracked ice and
strain into 3 oz. cocktail glass.*

LITTLE DEVIL COCKTAIL

Juice of ¼ Lemon
¼ oz. Triple Sec
¾ oz. Old Mr. Boston Imported
   Rum
¾ oz. Old Mr. Boston Dry Gin
*Shake well with cracked ice and
strain into 3 oz. cocktail glass.*

LITTLE PRINCESS COCKTAIL

1¼ oz. Sweet Vermouth
1¼ oz. Old Mr. Boston Imported
   Rum
*Stir well with cracked ice and strain
into 3 oz. cocktail glass.*

LONDON BUCK

1 Cube of Ice
2 oz. Old Mr. Boston Dry Gin
Juice of ½ Lemon
*Fill 8 oz. highball glass with ginger
ale and stir gently.*

LONDON COCKTAIL

2 oz. Old Mr. Boston Dry Gin
2 Dashes Orange Bitters
½ Teaspoon Simple Syrup
½ Teaspoon Maraschino
*Stir well with cracked ice and strain
into 3 oz. cocktail glass. Add twist of
lemon peel to glass.*

LONDON SPECIAL COCKTAIL

*Put rind of ½ orange into 6 oz.
Champagne glass. Add:*
1 Lump Sugar
2 Dashes Bitters
*Fill with Champagne, well chilled,
and stir gently.*

59

L

LONE TREE COCKTAIL

¾ oz. Sweet Vermouth
1½ oz. Old Mr. Boston Dry Gin
Stir well with cracked ice and strain into 3 oz. cocktail glass.

LONE TREE COOLER

Into 12 oz. Tom Collins glass, put:
½ Teaspoon Powdered Sugar
2 oz. Carbonated Water
Stir and fill glass with cracked ice and add:
2 oz. Old Mr. Boston Dry Gin
½ oz. Dry Vermouth
Fill with carbonated water or ginger ale and stir again. Insert spiral of orange or lemon peel (or both) and dangle end over rim of glass.

LOS ANGELES COCKTAIL

Juice of ½ Lemon
1 Teaspoon Powdered Sugar
1 Egg
¼ Teaspoon Sweet Vermouth
1½ oz. Old Mr. Boston Whiskey*
Shake well with cracked ice and strain into 4 oz. cocktail glass.

LOVE COCKTAIL

2 oz. Old Mr. Boston Sloe Gin
White of 1 Egg
½ Teaspoon Lemon Juice
½ Teaspoon Raspberry Juice
Shake well with cracked ice and strain into 4 oz. cocktail glass.

LOVING CUP

Use large Glass Pitcher.
4 Teaspoons Powdered Sugar
6 oz. Carbonated Water
1 oz. Triple Sec
2 oz. Old Mr. Boston Five Star Brandy
Fill pitcher with cubes of ice. Add 1 pint Claret. Stir well and decorate with as many fruits as available and also rind of cucumber inserted on each side of pitcher. Top with small bunch of mint sprigs.

LUXURY COCKTAIL

3 oz. Old Mr. Boston Five Star Brandy
2 Dashes Orange Bitters
3 oz. well chilled Champagne
Stir very gently. Use 6 oz. Saucer Champagne glass.

* *Bourbon, Blended, Rye or Canadian.*

M

MAIDEN'S BLUSH COCKTAIL

¼ Teaspoon Lemon Juice
1 Teaspoon Curacao
1 Teaspoon Grenadine
1½ oz. Old Mr. Boston Dry Gin
Shake well with cracked ice and strain into 3 oz. cocktail glass.

MAI-TAI

½ Teaspoon Powdered Sugar
2 oz. Old Mr. Boston Imported
    Rum
1 oz. Curacao
½ oz. Orgeat or any almond
    flavored syrup
½ oz. Grenadine
½ oz. Fresh Lime Juice
Shake well with cracked ice and strain into large Old Fashioned cocktail glass about ⅓ full with crushed ice. Decorate with Maraschino cherry speared to wedge of preferably fresh pineapple. For a hair raiser top with a dash of 151 proof rum and for a real Hawaiian effect float an orchid on each drink. Serve with straws.

MAJOR BAILEY

¼ oz. Lime Juice
¼ oz. Lemon Juice
½ Teaspoon Powdered Sugar
12 Mint Leaves
Muddle well and pour into 12 oz. Tom Collins glass filled with shaved ice, and add: 2 oz. Old Mr. Boston Dry Gin. *Stir gently, until glass is frosted. Decorate with spring of mint and serve with straws.*

MAMIE GILROY

Juice ½ Lime
2 Cubes of Ice
2 oz. Old Mr. Boston Scotch
    Whisky
1 Dash Bitters
Fill 12 oz. Tom Collins glass with carbonated water and stir gently.

MAMIE TAYLOR

Juice ½ Lime
2 Cubes of Ice
2 oz. Old Mr. Boston Scotch
    Whisky
Fill 12 oz. Tom Collins glass with ginger ale and stir gently.

M

MAMIE'S SISTER
Juice 1 Lime
Drop rind in glass.
2 Cubes of Ice
2 oz. Old Mr. Boston Dry Gin
Fill 12 oz. Tom Collins glass with ginger ale and stir gently.

MANHATTAN COCKTAIL
1 Dash Bitters
¾ oz. Sweet Vermouth
1½ oz. Old Mr. Boston Whiskey*
Stir well with cracked ice and strain into 3 oz. cocktail glass. Serve with a cherry.

MANHATTAN COCKTAIL (Dry)
1 Dash Bitters
¾ oz. Dry Vermouth
1½ oz. Old Mr. Boston Whiskey*
Stir well with cracked ice and strain into 3 oz. cocktail glass. Serve with an olive.

MANHATTAN COCKTAIL (Sweet)
1 Dash Bitters
¾ oz. Sweet Vermouth
1½ oz. Old Mr. Boston Whiskey*
Stir well with cracked ice and strain into 3 oz. cocktail glass. Serve with a cherry.

MANILA FIZZ
2 oz. Old Mr. Boston Dry Gin
1 Egg
1 Teaspoon Powdered Sugar
2 oz. Sarsaparilla
Juice of 1 Lime or ½ Lemon
Shake well with cracked ice and strain into 10 oz. Pilsner glass.

MARGARITA COCKTAIL
1½ oz. Tequila
½ oz. Triple Sec
Juice of ½ Lemon or Lime
Stir with crushed ice. Rub rim of 3 oz. cocktail glass with rind of lemon or lime, dip rim in salt, pour and serve.

MARTINEZ COCKTAIL
1 Dash Orange Bitters
1 oz. Dry Vermouth
¼ Teaspoon Curacao
1 oz. Old Mr. Boston Dry Gin
Stir well with cracked ice and strain into 3 oz. cocktail glass. Serve with a cherry.

MARTINI COCKTAIL
See *Special Martini Section* on pages 116 and 117.

MARY GARDEN COCKTAIL
1½ oz. Dubonnet
¾ oz. Dry Vermouth
Stir well with cracked ice and strain into 3 oz. cocktail glass.

MARY PICKFORD COCKTAIL
1 oz. Old Mr. Boston Imported Rum
1 oz. Pineapple Juice
¼ Teaspoon Grenadine
¼ Teaspoon Maraschino
Shake well with cracked ice and strain into 3 oz. cocktail glass.

* *Bourbon, Blended, Rye or Canadian.*

M

MAURICE COCKTAIL

Juice of ¼ Orange
½ oz. Sweet Vermouth
½ oz. Dry Vermouth
1 oz. Old Mr. Boston Dry Gin
1 Dash Bitters
Shake well with cracked ice and strain into 4 oz. cocktail glass.

MAY BLOSSOM FIZZ

1 Teaspoon Grenadine
Juice ½ Lemon
2 oz. Swedish Punch
Shake well with cracked ice and strain into 7 oz. highball glass. Fill with carbonated water and stir.

McCLELLAND COCKTAIL

¾ oz. Curacao
1½ oz. Old Mr. Boston Sloe Gin
1 Dash Orange Bitters
Shake well with cracked ice and strain into 3 oz. cocktail glass.

MELON COCKTAIL

2 oz. Old Mr. Boston Dry Gin
¼ Teaspoon Lemon Juice
¼ Teaspoon Maraschino
Shake well with cracked ice and strain into 3 oz. cocktail glass. Serve with a cherry.

MERRY WIDOW COCKTAIL No. 1

¼ oz. Old Mr. Boston Dry Gin
¼ oz. Dry Vermouth
½ Teaspoon Benedictine
½ Teaspoon Absinthe Substitute
Dash Orange Bitters
Stir well with cracked ice and strain into 3 oz. cocktail glass. Add twist of lemon peel and drop in glass.

MERRY WIDOW COCKTAIL No. 2

1¼ oz. Maraschino
1¼ oz. Old Mr. Boston Wild Cherry Flavored Brandy
Stir well with cracked ice and strain into 3 oz. cocktail glass. Serve with a cherry.

MERRY WIDOW FIZZ

Juice ½ Orange
Juice ½ Lemon
White of 1 Egg
1 Teaspoon Powdered Sugar
1½ oz. Old Mr. Boston Sloe Gin
Shake well with cracked ice and strain into 8 oz. highball glass. Fill with carbonated water and stir.

METROPOLITAN COCKTAIL

1¼ oz. Old Mr. Boston Five Star Brandy
1¼ oz. Sweet Vermouth
½ Teaspoon Simple Syrup
1 Dash Bitters
Stir well with cracked ice and strain into 3 oz. cocktail glass.

MEXICOLA

2 oz. Tequila
Juice ½ Lime
Use 12 oz. Tom Collins glass with cubes of ice. Fill balance with cola and stir gently.

M

MIAMI BEACH COCKTAIL

¾ oz. Old Mr. Boston Scotch
  Whisky
¾ oz. Dry Vermouth
¾ oz. Grapefruit Juice
*Stir well with cracked ice and strain
into 3 oz. cocktail glass.*

MIDNIGHT COCKTAIL

1 oz. Old Mr. Boston Apricot
  Flavored Brandy
½ oz. Curacao
½ oz. Lemon Juice
*Shake well with cracked ice and
strain into 3 oz. cocktail glass.*

MIKADO COCKTAIL

2 oz. Old Mr. Boston Five Star
  Brandy
2 Dashes Bitters
½ Teaspoon Old Mr. Boston
  Creme de Cacao
½ Teaspoon Curacao
*Shake well with cracked ice and
strain into 3 oz. cocktail glass.*

MILK PUNCH

1 Teaspoon Powdered Sugar
2 oz. Old Mr. Boston Whiskey*
½ pt. Milk
*Shake well with cracked ice and
strain into 12 oz. Tom Collins glass.
Grate nutmeg on top.*

MILLION DOLLAR COCKTAIL

2 Teaspoons Pineapple Juice
1 Teaspoon Grenadine
White of 1 Egg
¾ oz. Sweet Vermouth
1½ oz. Old Mr. Boston Dry Gin
*Shake well with cracked ice and
strain into 4 oz. cocktail glass.*

MILLIONAIRE COCKTAIL

White of 1 Egg
¼ Teaspoon Grenadine
½ oz. Curacao
1½ oz. Old Mr. Boston Whiskey*
*Shake well with cracked ice and
strain into 4 oz. cocktail glass.*

MINT COLLINS

Juice ½ Lemon
2 oz. Old Mr. Boston Mint Flavored Gin
*Shake well with cracked ice and
strain into 12 oz. Tom Collins glass.
Add several cubes of ice, fill with carbonated water and stir. Decorate
with slice of lemon, orange and a
cherry. Serve with straws.*

MINT GIN COCKTAIL

1 oz. Old Mr. Boston Mint Fl
  vored Gin
1 oz. White Port Wine
¼ oz. Dry Vermouth
*Stir well with cracked ice and stra
into 3 oz. cocktail glass.*

MINT HIGHBALL

1 Cube of Ice
2 oz. Old Mr. Boston Creme d
  Menthe (green)
*Fill 8 oz. highball glass with ginge
ale or carbonated water. Add twis
of lemon peel, if desired, and stir.*

* *Bourbon, Blended, Rye or Canadian*

M

MINT JULEP

nto Silver Mug or 12 oz. Tom Col-
ins glass put:
- Sprigs of Mint
- Teaspoon Powdered Sugar
- Teaspoons of Water, and muddle
ill glass or mug with shaved ice,
dd 2½ oz. Old Mr. Boston Ken-
ucky Straight Bourbon Whiskey,
nd stir gently until glass is frosted.
*Decorate with slice of orange, lemon,
ineapple and a cherry Insert 5 or
 sprigs of mint on top. Serve with
traws.*

MINT JULEP (Southern Style)

*nto a silver mug or 12 ounce Tom
Collins glass, dissolve 1 teaspoon
owdered sugar with 2 teaspoons of
ater. Then fill with finely shaved
e and add 2½ ozs. Old Mr. Bos-
n Kentucky Straight Bourbon
Whiskey. Stir until glass is heavily
osted adding more ice if necessary.
Do not hold glass with hand while
irring.) Decorate with 5 or 6
rigs of fresh mint so that the tops
e about 2 inches above rim of mug
 glass. Use short straws so that it
ill be necessary to bury nose in
int. The mint is intended for odor
ther than taste.*

MINT ON ROCKS

*ur 2 oz. Old Mr. Boston Creme
 Menthe (green) on ice cubes in
ld Fashioned cocktail glass.*

MR. MANHATTAN COCKTAIL

Muddle lump of sugar and
4 Sprigs of Mint
¼ Teaspoon Lemon Juice
1 Teaspoon Orange Juice
1½ oz. Old Mr. Boston Dry Gin
*Shake well with cracked ice and
strain into 3 oz. cocktail glass.*

MODERN COCKTAIL

1½ oz. Old Mr. Boston Scotch
  Whisky
½ Teaspoon Lemon Juice
¼ Teaspoon Absinthe Substitute
½ Teaspoon Jamaica Rum
1 Dash Orange Bitters
*Shake well with cracked ice and
strain into 3 oz. cocktail glass. Serve
with a cherry.*

MONTE CARLO IMPERIAL HIGHBALL

2 oz. Old Mr. Boston Dry Gin
½ oz. Old Mr. Boston Creme de
  Menthe (white)
Juice ¼ Lemon
*Shake well with cracked ice and
strain into 8 oz. highball glass. Fill
glass with Champagne and stir.*

MONTMARTRE COCKTAIL

1¼ oz. Old Mr. Boston Dry Gin
½ oz. Sweet Vermouth
½ oz. Triple Sec
*Stir well with cracked ice and strain
into 3 oz. cocktail glass. Serve with a
cherry.*

M

Morning Cocktail

1 oz. Old Mr. Boston Five Star Brandy
1 oz. Dry Vermouth
¼ Teaspoon Curacao
¼ Teaspoon Maraschino
¼ Teaspoon Absinthe Substitute
2 Dashes Orange Bitters
Stir well with cracked ice and strain into 3 oz. cocktail glass. Serve with a cherry.

Morning Glory Fizz

Juice ½ Lemon or 1 Lime
1 Teaspoon Powdered Sugar
White of 1 Egg
½ Teaspoon Absinthe Substitute
2 oz. Old Mr. Boston Scotch Whisky
Shake well with cracked ice and strain into 8 oz. highball glass. Fill with carbonated water and stir.

Moscow Mule

Into a Copper Mug, put:
1½ oz. Old Mr. Boston Vodka
Juice of ½ Lime
Add ice cubes and fill with ginger beer. Drop lime in mug to decorate.

Moulin Rouge Cocktail

1½ oz. Old Mr. Boston Sloe Gin
¾ oz. Sweet Vermouth
1 Dash Bitters
Stir well with cracked ice and strain into 3 oz. cocktail glass.

Mountain Cocktail

White of 1 Egg
¼ Teaspoon Lemon Juice
¼ Teaspoon Dry Vermouth
¼ Teaspoon Sweet Vermouth
1½ oz. Old Mr. Boston Whiskey*
Shake well with cracked ice and strain into 4 oz. cocktail glass.

Mulled Claret

Into a metal mug put:
1 Lump Sugar
Juice ½ Lemon
1 Dash Bitters
1 Teaspoon Mixed Cinnamon and Nutmeg
5 oz. Claret
Heat poker red hot and hold in liquid until boiling and serve.

* *Bourbon, Blended, Rye or Canadian*

NAPOLEON COCKTAIL
2 oz. Old Mr. Boston Dry Gin
½ Teaspoon Curacao
½ Teaspoon Dubonnet
Stir well with cracked ice and strain into 3 oz. cocktail glass.

NEGRONIS
¾ oz. Old Mr. Boston Dry Gin
¾ oz. Campari Bitters
¾ oz. Sweet or Dry Vermouth
¾ oz. Soda Water
Pour over ice cubes in Old Fashioned cocktail glass and stir lightly.

NEVADA COCKTAIL
1½ oz. Old Mr. Boston Imported
  Rum
1 oz. Grapefruit Juice
Juice of 1 Lime
1 Dash Bitters
3 Teaspoons Powdered Sugar
Shake well with cracked ice and strain into 4 oz. cocktail glass.

NEW ORLEANS GIN FIZZ
Juice ½ Lemon
Juice ½ Lime (optional)
1 Teaspoon Powdered Sugar
White of 1 Egg
2 oz. Old Mr. Boston Dry Gin
1 Tablespoon Sweet Cream
½ Teaspoon Orange Flower Water
Shake well with cracked ice and strain into 12 oz. Tom Collins glass. Fill with carbonated water and stir.

NEW YORK COCKTAIL
Juice 1 Lime or ½ Lemon
1 Teaspoon Powdered Sugar
1½ oz. Old Mr. Boston Whiskey*
½ Teaspoon Grenadine
Twist of Orange Peel
Shake well with cracked ice and strain into 3 oz. cocktail glass. Add twist of lemon peel and drop in glass.

NEW YORK SOUR
Juice ½ Lemon
1 Teaspoon Powdered Sugar
2 oz. Old Mr. Boston Whiskey*
Shake well with cracked ice and strain into 6 oz. sour glass, leaving about ½ inch on which to float claret. Decorate with a half-slice of lemon and a cherry.

* *Bourbon, Blended, Rye or Canadian.*

O

NIGHT CAP

2 oz. Old Mr. Boston Imported
    Rum
1 Teaspoon Powdered Sugar
*Add enough warm milk to fill a Tom
& Jerry Mug and stir. Grate a little
nutmeg on top.*

NORTH POLE COCKTAIL

White of 1 Egg
½ oz. Lemon Juice
½ oz. Maraschino
1 oz. Old Mr. Boston Dry Gin
*Shake well with cracked ice and
strain into 4 oz. cocktail glass and
top with whipped cream.*

NINITCHKA COCKTAIL

1½ oz. Old Mr. Boston Vodka
½ oz. Old Mr. Boston Creme de
    Cacao
½ oz. Lemon Juice
*Shake well with cracked ice and
strain into 3 oz. cocktail glass.*

OLD FASHIONED COCKTAIL

Use Old Fashioned cocktail glass.
½ Lump of Sugar
2 Dashes Bitters
*Add enough water to cover sugar
and muddle well.*
1 Cube of Ice
2 oz. Old Mr. Boston Whiskey*
*Stir well. Add twist of lemon rind
and drop in glass. Decorate with
slice of orange, lemon and a cherry.
Serve with stirring rod.*

OLD PAL COCKTAIL

½ oz. Grenadine
½ oz. Sweet Vermouth
1¼ oz. Old Mr. Boston Whiskey*
*Stir well with cracked ice and strain
into 3 oz. cocktail glass.*

* Bourbon, Blended, Rye or Canadian.

O

OLYMPIC COCKTAIL

¾ oz. Orange Juice
¾ oz. Curacao
¾ oz. Old Mr. Boston Five Star Brandy
Shake well with cracked ice and strain into 3 oz. cocktail glass.

OPAL COCKTAIL

1 oz. Old Mr. Boston Dry Gin
½ oz. Orange Juice
½ oz. Triple Sec
¼ Teaspoon Powdered Sugar
½ Teaspoon Orange Flower Water
Shake well with cracked ice and strain into 3 oz. cocktail glass.

OPENING COCKTAIL

½ oz. Grenadine
½ oz. Sweet Vermouth
1¼ oz. Old Mr. Boston Whiskey*
Stir well with cracked ice and strain into 3 oz. cocktail glass.

OPERA COCKTAIL

½ oz. Maraschino
½ oz. Dubonnet
½ oz. Old Mr. Boston Dry Gin
Stir well with cracked ice and strain into 3 oz. cocktail glass.

ORANGEADE

Juice 2 Oranges
1 Teaspoon Powdered Sugar
Add 2 cubes of ice and enough water to fill 12 oz. Tom Collins glass and stir well. Decorate with a slice of orange, lemon and 2 cherries. Serve with straws.

ORANGE BLOSSOM COCKTAIL

1 oz. Old Mr. Boston Dry Gin
1 oz. Orange Juice
¼ Teaspoon Powdered Sugar
Shake well with cracked ice and strain into 3 oz. cocktail glass.

ORANGE GIN COLLINS

Juice ½ Lemon
2 oz. Old Mr. Boston Orange Flavored Gin
Shake well with cracked ice and strain into 12 oz. Tom Collins glass. Add several cubes of ice, fill with carbonated water and stir. Decorate with slice of lemon, orange and a cherry. Serve with straws.

ORANGE GIN FIZZ

Juice ½ Lemon
1 Teaspoon Powdered Sugar
2 oz. Old Mr. Boston Orange Flavored Gin
Shake well with cracked ice and strain into 7 oz. highball glass. Fill with carbonated water and stir.

ORANGE GIN HIGHBALL

1 Cube of Ice
2 oz. Old Mr. Boston Orange Flavored Gin
Fill 8 oz. highball glass with ginger ale or carbonated water. Add twist of lemon peel, if desired, and stir.

*Bourbon, Blended, Rye or Canadian.

Orange Gin Rickey

1 Cube of Ice
Juice ½ Lime
2 oz. Old Mr. Boston Orange Flavored Gin
Fill 8 oz. highball glass with carbonated water and stir. Leave lime in glass.

Orange Milk Fizz

Juice ½ Lemon
1 Teaspoon Powdered Sugar
2 oz. Old Mr. Boston Orange Flavored Gin
2 oz. Milk
Shake well with cracked ice and strain into 8 oz. highball glass. Fill with carbonated water and stir.

Orange Smile

1 Egg
Juice 1 Large Orange
1 Tablespoon Raspberry Syrup or Grenadine
Shake well with cracked ice and strain into 8 oz. stem goblet.

Orchid Cocktail

2 oz. Old Mr. Boston Dry Gin
1 Egg White
1 Dash of Creme de Yvette
Shake well with cracked ice and strain into 4 oz. cocktail glass.

Oriental Cocktail

1 oz. Old Mr. Boston Whiskey*
½ oz. Sweet Vermouth
½ oz. Curacao
Juice of ½ Lime
Shake well with cracked ice and strain into 3 oz. cocktail glass.

Paddy Cocktail

1¼ oz. Irish Whiskey
1¼ oz. Sweet Vermouth
1 Dash Bitters
Stir well with cracked ice and strain into 3 oz. cocktail glass.

Palm Beach Cocktail

1½ oz. Old Mr. Boston Dry Gin
¼ oz. Sweet Vermouth
¼ oz. Grapefruit Juice
Shake well with cracked ice and strain into 3 oz. cocktail glass.

71

* *Bourbon, Blended, Rye or Canadian.*

P

PALMER COCKTAIL

2 oz. Old Mr. Boston Whiskey*
1 Dash Bitters
½ Teaspoon Lemon Juice
Stir well with cracked ice and strain into 3 oz. cocktail glass.

PALMETTO COCKTAIL

1¼ oz. Old Mr. Boston Imported Rum
1¼ oz. Dry Vermouth
2 Dashes Bitters
Stir well with cracked ice and strain into 3 oz. cocktail glass.

PANAMA COCKTAIL

1 oz. Old Mr. Boston Creme de Cacao
1 oz. Sweet Cream
1 oz. Old Mr. Boston Five Star Brandy
Shake well with cracked ice and strain into 4 oz. cocktail glass.

PARADISE COCKTAIL

1 oz. Old Mr. Boston Apricot Flavored Brandy
¾ oz. Old Mr. Boston Dry Gin
Juice ¼ Orange
Shake well with cracked ice and strain into 3 oz. cocktail glass.

PARISIAN BLONDE COCKTAIL

¾ oz. Sweet Cream
¾ oz. Curacao
¾ oz. Jamaica Rum
Shake well with cracked ice and strain into 3 oz. cocktail glass.

PASSION DAIQUIRI COCKTAIL

1½ oz. Old Mr. Boston Imported Rum
Juice 1 Lime
1 Teaspoon Powdered Sugar
½ oz. Passion Fruit Juice
Shake well with cracked ice and strain into 3 oz. cocktail glass.

PEACH BLOSSOM

1 Teaspoon Lemon Juice
½ Teaspoon Powdered Sugar
2 oz. Old Mr. Boston Dry Gin
½ Peach
Shake well with cracked ice and strain into 8 oz. highball glass. Fill with carbonated water and stir.

PEACH BLOW FIZZ

Juice ½ Lemon
White of 1 Egg
2 Teaspoons Grenadine
½ Teaspoon Powdered Sugar
1 oz. Sweet Cream
2 oz. Old Mr. Boston Dry Gin
Shake well with cracked ice and strain into 10 oz. highball glass. Fill with carbonated water and stir.

PEACH SANGAREE

2 oz. Old Mr. Boston Peach Flavored Brandy
2 cubes of Ice
Serve in 8 oz. highball glass. Fill balance with soda water. Stir, leaving enough room on which to float tablespoon of Port Wine. Sprinkle lightly with nutmeg.

* *Bourbon, Blended, Rye or Canadian*

P

PEGGY COCKTAIL
¾ oz. Dry Vermouth
1½ oz. Old Mr. Boston Dry Gin
¼ Teaspoon Absinthe Substitute
¼ Teaspoon Dubonnet
Stir well with cracked ice and strain into 3 oz. cocktail glass.

PENDENNIS TODDY
Muddle lump of sugar with 1 teaspoon of water, in 6 oz. sour glass. Fill with finely shaved ice, add 2 oz. Old Mr. Boston Whiskey* and stir. Decorate with 2 slices of lemon.

PERFECT COCKTAIL
¼ oz. Dry Vermouth
¼ oz. Sweet Vermouth
1½ oz. Old Mr. Boston Dry Gin
1 Dash Bitters
Stir well with cracked ice and strain into 3 oz. cocktail glass.

PETER PAN COCKTAIL
2 Dashes Bitters
¾ oz. Orange Juice
¾ oz. Dry Vermouth
¾ oz. Old Mr. Boston Dry Gin
Shake well with cracked ice and strain into 3 oz. cocktail glass.

PHOEBE SNOW COCKTAIL
1¼ oz. Dubonnet
1¼ oz. Old Mr. Boston Five Star Brandy
¼ Teaspoon Absinthe Substitute
Stir well with cracked ice and strain into 3 oz. cocktail glass.

PICCADILLY COCKTAIL
¾ oz. Dry Vermouth
1½ oz. Old Mr. Boston Dry Gin
¼ Teaspoon Absinthe Substitute
¼ Teaspoon Grenadine
Stir well with cracked ice and strain into 3 oz. cocktail glass.

PICON COCKTAIL
See AMER PICON COCKTAIL *on page 3.*

PIKE'S PEAK COOLER
Juice ½ Lemon
1 Teaspoon Powdered Sugar
1 Egg
Shake well with cracked ice and strain into 12 oz. Tom Collins glass and fill with hard cider and stir. Insert spiral of orange or lemon peel (or both) and dangle end over rim of glass.

PINEAPPLE COCKTAIL
¾ oz. Pineapple Juice
1½ oz. Old Mr. Boston Imported Rum
½ Teaspoon Lemon Juice
Shake well with cracked ice and strain into 3 oz. cocktail glass.

PINEAPPLE COOLER
Into 12 oz. Tom Collins glass, put:
2 oz. Pineapple Juice
½ Teaspoon Powdered Sugar
2 oz. Carbonated Water
Stir; fill glass with cracked ice and add: 2 oz. Dry White Wine. Fill with carbonated water and stir again. Insert spiral of orange or lemon peel (or both) and dangle end over rim of glass.

73

* *Bourbon, Blended, Rye or Canadian.*

P

PINEAPPLE FIZZ

1 oz. Pineapple Juice
½ Teaspoon Powdered Sugar
2 oz. Old Mr. Boston Imported Rum
Shake well with cracked ice and strain into 7 oz. highball glass. Fill with carbonated water and stir.

PING-PONG COCKTAIL

Juice of ¼ Lemon
White of 1 Egg
1 oz. Old Mr. Boston Sloe Gin
1 oz. Creme de Yvette
Shake well with cracked ice and strain into 4 oz. cocktail glass.

PINK PUSSY CAT

Use 7 oz. Highball glass almost filled with shaved ice and add:
1½ oz. Old Mr. Boston Vodka or Dry Gin
Fill balance of glass with pineapple or grapefruit juice. Add dash of Grenadine for color and stir.

PINK GIN

See GIN AND BITTERS *page 40.*

PINK LADY COCKTAIL

White of 1 Egg
1 Teaspoon Grenadine
1 Teaspoon Sweet Cream
1½ oz. Old Mr. Boston Dry Gin
Shake well with cracked ice and strain into 4 oz. cocktail glass.

PINK ROSE FIZZ

Juice ½ Lemon
1 Teaspoon Powdered Sugar
White of 1 Egg
½ Teaspoon Grenadine
2 Teaspoons Sweet Cream
2 oz. Old Mr. Boston Dry Gin
Shake well with cracked ice and strain into 8 oz. highball glass. Fill with carbonated water and stir.

PINK SQUIRREL COCKTAIL

1 oz. Creme de Almond Liqueur
½ oz. Old Mr. Boston Creme de Cacao (white)
½ oz. Light Cream
Shake well with cracked ice and strain into 3 oz. cocktail glass.

PLAIN VERMOUTH COCKTAIL

See VERMOUTH COCKTAIL *page 103.*

PLANTER'S COCKTAIL

Juice of ¼ Lemon
½ Teaspoon Powdered Sugar
1½ oz. Jamaica Rum
Shake well with cracked ice and strain into 3 oz. cocktail glass.

74

P

PLANTER'S PUNCH No. 1

Juice 2 Limes
2 Teaspoons Powdered Sugar
2 oz. Carbonated Water
*Fill 12 oz. Tom Collins glass with
shaved ice and stir until glass is
frosted. Add 2 dashes Bitters,* 2½ oz.
Old Mr. Boston Imported Rum.
*Stir and decorate with slice of lemon,
orange, pineapple and a cherry.
Serve with straws.*

PLANTER'S PUNCH No. 2

Juice 1 Lime
Juice ½ Lemon
Juice ½ Orange
1 Teaspoon Pineapple Juice
2 oz. Old Mr. Boston Imported
    Rum
*Pour above into 16 oz. glass, well
filled with shaved ice. Stir until glass
is frosted. Then add* 1 oz. Jamaica
Rum, *and top with* ¼ teaspoon
Curacao. *Decorate with slice of orange, lemon, pineapple and a cherry,
also sprig of mint dipped in powdered sugar. Serve with straws.*

PLAZA COCKTAIL

¾ oz. Sweet Vermouth
¾ oz. Dry Vermouth
¾ oz. Old Mr. Boston Dry Gin
1 Strip of Pineapple
*Shake well with cracked ice and
strain into 3 oz. cocktail glass.*

POKER COCKTAIL

1¼ oz. Sweet Vermouth
1¼ oz. Old Mr. Boston Imported
    Rum
*Stir well with cracked ice and strain
into 3 oz. cocktail glass.*

POLLYANNA COCKTAIL

*Muddle 3 slices of orange and
slices of pineapple*
2 oz. Old Mr. Boston Dry Gin
½ oz. Sweet Vermouth
½ Teaspoon Grenadine
*Shake well with cracked ice an
strain into 4 oz. cocktail glass.*

POLO COCKTAIL

½ oz. Lemon Juice
½ oz. Orange Juice
1 oz. Old Mr. Boston Dry Gin
*Shake well with cracked ice an
strain into 3 oz. cocktail glass.*

POLYNESIAN COCKTAIL

1½ oz. Old Mr. Boston Vodka
¾ oz. Old Mr. Boston Wild Cherr
    Flavored Brandy
Juice of 1 Lime
*Shake well with cracked ice an
strain into 4 oz. cocktail glass. Fro:
rim by rubbing with lime and di
ping in powdered sugar.*

POOP DECK COCKTAIL

1¼ oz. Old Mr. Boston Blackberr
    Flavored Brandy
½ oz. Port Wine
½ oz. Old Mr. Boston Five Sta
    Brandy
*Stir well with cracked ice and strai:
into 3 oz. cocktail glass.*

POPPY COCKTAIL

¾ oz. Old Mr. Boston Creme d
    Cacao
1½ oz. Old Mr. Boston Dry Gin
*Shake well with cracked ice an
strain into 3 oz. cocktail glass.*

P

PORT AND STARBOARD

½ oz. Grenadine
½ oz. Old Mr. Boston Creme de Menthe (green)
Pour carefully into Pousse Café glass, so that Menthe floats on Grenadine.

PORT MILK PUNCH

1 Teaspoon Powdered Sugar
3 oz. Port Wine
½ pt. Milk
Shake well with cracked ice, strain into 12 oz. Tom Collins glass and grate nutmeg on top.

PORT WINE COBBLER

Dissolve 1 teaspoon powdered sugar in 2 oz. carbonated water; then fill 10 oz. goblet with shaved ice and add 3 oz. Port Wine. Stir well and decorate with fruits in season. Serve with straws.

PORT WINE COCKTAIL

2¼ oz. Port Wine
½ Teaspoon Old Mr. Boston Five Star Brandy
Stir slightly with cracked ice and strain into 3 oz. cocktail glass.

PORT WINE EGGNOG

1 Egg
1 Teaspoon Powdered Sugar
3 oz. Port Wine
Fill glass with milk. Shake well with cracked ice and strain into 12 oz. Tom Collins glass. Grate nutmeg on top.

PORT WINE FLIP

1 Egg
1 Teaspoon Powdered Sugar
1½ oz. Port Wine
2 Teaspoons Sweet Cream (if desired)
Shake well with cracked ice and strain into 5 oz. flip glass. Grate a little nutmeg on top.

PORT WINE NEGUS

½ Lump Sugar
2 oz. Port Wine
Fill hot whiskey glass with hot water and stir. Grate nutmeg on top.

PORT WINE SANGAREE

Dissolve ½ teaspoon powdered sugar in 1 teaspoon of water.
2 oz. Port Wine
2 cubes of Ice
Serve in 8 oz. highball glass. Fill balance with soda water. Stir, leaving enough room on which to float a tablespoon of Brandy. Sprinkle lightly with nutmeg.

POUSSE CAFÉ

⅙ Grenadine
⅙ Yellow Chartreuse
⅙ Creme de Yvette
⅙ Old Mr. Boston Creme de Menthe (white)
⅙ Green Chartreuse
⅙ Old Mr. Boston Five Star Brandy
Pour carefully, in order given, into Pousse Café glass so that each ingredient floats on preceding one.

See Index on page 145 for complete list of Pousse Café recipes.

POUSSE L'AMOUR

⅓ oz. Maraschino
Yolk of 1 Egg
⅓ oz. Benedictine
⅓ oz. Old Mr. Boston Five Star Brandy
Pour carefully, in order given, into 2 oz. Sherry glass, so that each ingredient floats on preceding one.

PRAIRIE HEN COCKTAIL

1 Whole Egg
1 Teaspoon Worcestershire Sauce
½ Teaspoon Vinegar
1 Drop Tabasco Sauce
Season with a little salt and pepper. Use 5 oz. Delmonico glass.

PRAIRIE OYSTER COCKTAIL

1 Whole Egg
1 Teaspoon Worcestershire Sauce
1 Teaspoon Tomato Catsup
½ Teaspoon Vinegar
Pinch of Pepper
1 Drop Tabasco Sauce
Use 5 oz. Delmonico glass.

PREAKNESS COCKTAIL

¾ oz. Sweet Vermouth
1½ oz. Old Mr. Boston Whiskey*
1 Dash Bitters
½ Teaspoon Benedictine
Stir well with cracked ice and strain into 3 oz. cocktail glass. Add twist of lemon peel and drop in glass.

PRESTO COCKTAIL

½ oz. Orange Juice
½ oz. Sweet Vermouth
1¼ oz. Old Mr. Boston Five Star Brandy
¼ Teaspoon Absinthe Substitute
Shake well with cracked ice and strain into 3 oz. cocktail glass.

PRINCE'S SMILE COCKTAIL

½ oz. Old Mr. Boston Apricot Flavored Brandy
½ oz. Apple Brandy
1 oz. Old Mr. Boston Dry Gin
¼ Teaspoon Lemon Juice
Shake well with cracked ice and strain into 3 oz. cocktail glass.

PRINCESS POUSSE CAFE

¾ oz. Old Mr. Boston Apricot Flavored Brandy
¼ oz. Sweet Cream
Pour cream carefully on top, so that it does not mix. Use Pousse Cafe glass.

PRINCETON COCKTAIL

1 oz. Old Mr. Boston Dry Gin
1 oz. Dry Vermouth
Juice ½ Lime
Stir well with cracked ice and strain into 3 oz. cocktail glass.

PUNCHES

See Index on page 145 for complete list of PUNCH recipes.

* *Bourbon, Blended, Rye or Canadian*

QUAKER'S COCKTAIL

¾ oz. Old Mr. Boston Imported
  Rum
¾ oz. Old Mr. Boston Five Star
  Brandy
Juice ¼ Lemon
2 Teaspoons Raspberry Syrup
*Shake well with cracked ice and
strain into 3 oz. cocktail glass.*

QUARTER DECK COCKTAIL

⅓ oz. Sherry Wine
1½ oz. Old Mr. Boston Imported
  Rum
Juice ½ Lime
*Stir well with cracked ice and strain
into 3 oz. cocktail glass.*

QUEEN CHARLOTTE

2 oz. Claret Wine
1 oz. Raspberry Syrup or Grenadine
*Pour into 12 oz. Tom Collins glass.
Add cub of ice; fill with lemon soda
and stir.*

QUEEN ELIZABETH COCKTAIL

1½ oz. Old Mr. Boston Dry Gin
½ oz. Dry Vermouth
¼ oz. Benedictine
*Stir well with cracked ice and strain
into 3 oz. cocktail glass.*

R

RACQUET CLUB COCKTAIL

1½ oz. Old Mr. Boston Dry Gin
¾ oz. Dry Vermouth
1 Dash Orange Bitters
Stir well with cracked ice and strain into 3 oz. cocktail glass.

RAMOS FIZZ

Juice ½ Lemon
White of 1 Egg
1 Teaspoon Powdered Sugar
2 oz. Old Mr. Boston Dry Gin
1 Tablespoon Sweet Cream
½ Teaspoon Orange Flower Water
Shake well with cracked ice and strain into 12 oz. Tom Collins glass. Fill with carbonated water and stir.

RATTLESNAKE COCKTAIL

1½ oz. Old Mr. Boston Whiskey*
White of 1 Egg
1 Teaspoon Lemon Juice
½ Teaspoon Powdered Sugar
¼ Teaspoon Absinthe Substitute
Shake well with cracked ice and strain into 4 oz. cocktail glass.

RED SWIZZLE

Make same as GIN SWIZZLE *(see page 43), and add 1 tablespoon of grenadine. If desired, rum, brandy or whiskey may be substituted for the gin.*

REFORM COCKTAIL

¾ oz. Dry Vermouth
1½ oz. Sherry Wine
1 Dash Orange Bitters
Stir well with cracked ice and strain into 3 oz. cocktail glass. Serve with a cherry.

REMSEN COOLER

Into 12 oz. Tom Collins glass, put:
½ Teaspoon Powdered Sugar
2 oz. Carbonated Water
Stir; fill glass with Cracked Ice and add:
2 oz. Old Mr. Boston Dry Gin
Fill with carbonated water or ginger ale and stir again. Insert spiral of orange or lemon peel (or both) and dangle end over rim of glass.

* *Bourbon, Blended, Rye or Canadian.*

R

RESOLUTE COCKTAIL

Juice ¼ Lemon
½ oz. Old Mr. Boston Apricot Flavored Brandy
1 oz. Old Mr. Boston Dry Gin
Shake well with cracked ice and strain into 3 oz. cocktail glass.

RHINE WINE CUP

Use Large Glass Pitcher
4 Teaspoons Powdered Sugar
6 oz. Carbonated Water
½ oz. Triple Sec
½ oz. Curacao
2 oz. Old Mr. Boston Five Star Brandy
Fill pitcher with cubes of ice. Add 1 pint of Rhine wine. Stir well and decorate with as many fruits as available and also rind of cucumber inserted on each side of pitcher. Top with small bunch of mint sprigs. Serve in 5 oz. Claret glass.

RICKIES

See Index on page 145 for complete list of RICKEY *recipes.*

ROB ROY COCKTAIL

¾ oz. Sweet Vermouth
1½ oz. Old Mr. Boston Scotch Whisky
1 Dash Orange Bitters
Stir well with cracked ice and strain into 3 oz. cocktail glass.

ROBERT E. LEE COOLER

Into 12 oz. Tom Collins glass, put:
Juice ½ Lime
½ Teaspoon Powdered Sugar
2 oz. Carbonated Water, and stir
Fill glass with cracked ice and add:
¼ Teaspoon Absinthe Substitute
2 oz. Old Mr. Boston Dry Gin
Fill with ginger ale and stir again. Insert spiral of orange or lemon peel (or both) and dangle end over rim of glass.

ROBSON COCKTAIL

2 Teaspoons Lemon Juice
½ oz. Orange Juice
¼ oz. Grenadine
1 oz. Jamaica Rum
Shake well with cracked ice and strain into 3 oz. cocktail glass.

ROCK & RYE COCKTAIL

1 oz. Old Mr. Boston Rock & Rye
1 oz. White Port Wine
¼ oz. Dry Vermouth
Stir well with cracked ice and strain into 3 oz. cocktail glass.

ROLLS-ROYCE COCKTAIL

½ oz. Dry Vermouth
½ oz. Sweet Vermouth
1¼ oz. Old Mr. Boston Dry Gin
¼ Teaspoon Benedictine
Stir well with cracked ice and strain into 3 oz. cocktail glass.

ROMA COCKTAIL

1 oz. Old Mr. Boston Dry Gin
½ oz. Dry Vermouth
½ oz. Sweet Vermouth
Add 2 or 3 strawberries. Shake well with cracked ice and strain into 3 oz. cocktail glass.

R

RORY O'MORE

¾ oz. Sweet Vermouth
1½ oz. Irish Whiskey
1 Dash Orange Bitters
*Stir well with cracked ice and strain
into 3 oz. cocktail glass.*

ROSE COCKTAIL (English)

½ oz. Old Mr. Boston Apricot Flavored Brandy
½ oz. Dry Vermouth
1 oz. Old Mr. Boston Dry Gin
½ Teaspoon Lemon Juice
1 Teaspoon Grenadine
*Shake well with cracked ice and
strain into 3 oz. cocktail glass. Frost
edge of glass by rubbing with lemon
and dipping in powdered sugar.*

ROSE COCKTAIL (French)

½ oz. Old Mr. Boston Wild Cherry
Flavored Brandy
½ oz. Dry Vermouth
1¼ oz. Old Mr. Boston Dry Gin
*Stir well with cracked ice and strain
into 3 oz. cocktail glass.*

ROSELYN COCKTAIL

¾ oz. Dry Vermouth
1½ oz. Old Mr. Boston Dry Gin
½ Teaspoon Grenadine
*Stir well with cracked ice and strain
into 3 oz. cocktail glass. Twist of
lemon peel on top and drop in glass.*

ROYAL CLOVER CLUB COCKTAIL

Juice 1 Lime
1 Tablespoon Grenadine
Yolk 1 Egg
1½ oz. Old Mr. Boston Dry Gin
*Shake well with cracked ice and
strain into 4 oz. cocktail glass.*

ROYAL COCKTAIL

1 Whole Egg
Juice ½ Lemon
1 Teaspoon Powdered Sugar
1½ oz. Old Mr. Boston Dry Gin
*Shake well with cracked ice and
strain into 4 oz. cocktail glass.*

ROYAL FIZZ

Juice ½ Lemon
1 Teaspoon Powdered Sugar
2 oz. Old Mr. Boston Dry Gin
1 Whole Egg
*Shake well with cracked ice and
strain into 8 oz. highball glass. Fill
with carbonated water and stir.*

ROYAL PURPLE PUNCH

*Pour 2 large bottles (⅘ quart size)
Claret Wine and 2 large bottles ginger ale over ice cubes in punch bowl.
Stir well. Float thin slices of lemon
studded with cloves on top. Serve in
4 oz. punch glasses.*

ROYAL SMILE COCKTAIL

Juice ¼ Lemon
1 Teaspoon Grenadine
½ oz. Old Mr. Boston Dry Gin
1 oz. Apple Brandy
*Stir well with cracked ice and strain
into 3 oz. cocktail glass.*

RUBY FIZZ

Juice ½ Lemon
1 Teaspoon Powdered Sugar
White of 1 Egg
1 Teaspoon Grenadine
2 oz. Old Mr. Boston Sloe Gin
*Shake well with cracked ice and
strain into 8 oz. highball glass. Fill
with carbonated water and stir.*

R

Rum Cobbler

Dissolve, in a 10 oz. goblet,
1 Teaspoon Powdered Sugar
2 oz. Carbonated Water
Fill goblet with shaved ice, and add:
2 oz. Old Mr. Boston Imported
　Rum
Stir well and decorate with fruits in season. Serve with straws.

Rum Cola

See Cuba Libra *Page 29.*

Rum Collins

Juice 1 Lime
1 Teaspoon Powdered Sugar
2 oz. Old Mr. Boston Imported
　Rum
Shake well with cracked ice and strain into 12 oz. Tom Collins glass. Add several cubes of ice, fill with carbonated water and stir. Decorate with slice of lemon and a cherry and drop lime in glass. Serve with straws.

Rum Cooler

Into 12 oz. Tom Collins glass, put:
½ Teaspoon Powdered Sugar
2 oz. Carbonated Water
Stir; fill glass with cracked ice and add:
2 oz. Old Mr. Boston Imported
　Rum
Fill with carbonated water or ginger ale and stir again. Insert spiral of orange or lemon peel (or both) and dangle end over rim of glass.

Rum Daisy

Juice of ½ Lemon
½ Teaspoon Powdered Sugar
1 Teaspoon Raspberry Syrup or
　Grenadine
2 oz. Old Mr. Boston Imported
　Rum
Shake well with cracked ice and strain into Stein or 8 oz. metal cup. Add cube of ice and decorate with fruit.

Rum Eggnog

1 Egg
1 Teaspoon Powdered Sugar
2 oz. Old Mr. Boston Imported
　Rum
Fill glass with milk. Shake well with cracked ice and strain into 12 oz. Tom Collins glass. Grate nutmeg on top.

Rum Fix

Juice ½ Lemon or 1 Lime
1 Teaspoon Powdered Sugar
1 Teaspoon Water and stir
Fill glass with Shaved Ice
2½ oz. Old Mr. Boston Imported
　Rum
Use 8 oz. highball glass. Stir well. Add slice of lemon. Serve with straws.

Rum Highball

1 Cube of Ice
2 oz. Old Mr. Boston Imported
　Rum
Fill 8 oz. highball glass with ginger ale or carbonated water. Add twist of lemon peel, if desired, and stir.

Rum Milk Punch

1 Teaspoon Powdered Sugar
2 oz. Old Mr. Boston Imported Rum
½ pt. Milk
Shake well with cracked ice, strain into 12 oz. Tom Collins glass and grate nutmeg on top.

Rum Rickey

1 Cube of Ice
Juice ½ Lime
1½ oz. Old Mr. Boston Imported Rum
Fill 8 oz. highball glass with carbonated water and stir. Leave lime in glass.

Rum Sour

Juice ½ Lemon
½ Teaspoon Powdered Sugar
2 oz. Old Mr. Boston Imported Rum
Shake well with cracked ice and strain into 6 oz. sour glass. Decorate with a half-slice of lemon and a cherry.

Rum Swizzle

Made same as Gin Swizzle *(see page 43), using* 2 oz. Old Mr. Boston Imported Rum.

Rum Toddy

Use Old Fashioned cocktail glass.
½ Teaspoon Powdered Sugar
2 Teaspoons Water
Stir.
2 oz. Old Mr. Boston Imported Rum
1 Lump of Ice
Stir again and twist lemon peel on top.

Rum Toddy (Hot)

Put lump of sugar into hot Whiskey glass and fill two-thirds with boiling water. Add 2 oz. Old Mr. Boston Imported Rum. *Stir and decorate with slice of lemon. Grate nutmeg on top.*

Russian Bear Cocktail

1 oz. Old Mr. Boston Vodka
½ oz. Old Mr. Boston Creme de Cacao
½ oz. Sweet Cream
Stir well with cracked ice and strain into 3 oz. cocktail glass.

Russian Cocktail

¾ oz. Old Mr. Boston Creme de Cacao
¾ oz. Old Mr. Boston Dry Gin
¾ oz. Old Mr. Boston Vodka
Shake well with cracked ice and strain into 3 oz. cocktail glass.

Rusty Nail

¾ oz. Old Mr. Boston Scotch Whiskey
¾ oz. Drambuie
Serve in Old Fashioned cocktail glass with cubes of ice.

Rye Highball

1 Cube of Ice
2 oz. Old Mr. Boston Rye Whiskey
Fill 8 oz. highball glass with ginger ale or carbonated water. Add twist of lemon peel, if desired, and stir.

Rye Whiskey Cocktail

1 Dash Bitters
1 Teaspoon Simple Syrup
2 oz. Old Mr. Boston Rye Whiskey
Stir well with cracked ice and strain into 3 oz. cocktail glass. Serve with a cherry.

S

St. Patrick's Day Cocktail

¾ oz. Old Mr. Boston Creme de Menthe (green)
¾ oz. Green Chartreuse
¾ oz. Irish Whiskey
1 Dash Bitters
Stir well with cracked ice and strain into 3 oz. cocktail glass.

Salty Dog

Fill 12 oz. Tom Collins glass almost full with shaved ice or ice cubes and add:
2 oz. Old Mr. Boston Dry Gin
2 oz. Grapefruit, Lemon or Lime Juice
¼ Teaspoon Salt
Stir well.

San Francisco Cocktail

¾ oz. Old Mr. Boston Sloe Gin
¾ oz. Sweet Vermouth
¾ oz. Dry Vermouth
1 Dash Bitters
1 Dash Orange Bitters
Shake well with cracked ice and strain into 3 oz. cocktail glass. Serve with a cherry.

Sand-Martin Cocktail

1 Teaspoon Green Chartreuse
1¼ oz. Sweet Vermouth
1¼ oz. Old Mr. Boston Dry Gin
Stir well with cracked ice and strain into 3 oz. cocktail glass.

Sangarees

See Index on page 146 for complete list of Sangaree *recipes.*

Santiago Cocktail

½ Teaspoon Powdered Sugar
¼ Teaspoon Grenadine
Juice 1 Lime
1½ oz. Old Mr. Boston Imported Rum
Shake well with cracked ice and strain into 3 oz. cocktail glass.

Saratoga Cocktail

2 oz. Old Mr. Boston Five Star Brandy
2 Dashes Bitters
½ Teaspoon Pineapple Syrup
½ Teaspoon Maraschino
Stir well with cracked ice and strain into 3 oz. cocktail glass.

Saratoga Cooler

Fill 12 oz. Tom Collins glass with cracked ice. Fill with sarsaparilla. Insert spiral of lemon and dangle end over rim of glass.

Saucy Sue Cocktail

½ Teaspoon Old Mr. Boston
   Apricot Flavored Brandy
½ Teaspoon Absinthe Substitute
2 oz. Apple Brandy
*Stir well with cracked ice and strain
into 3 oz. cocktail glass.*

Sauterne Cup

Use large glass pitcher.
4 Teaspoons Powdered Sugar
6 oz. Carbonated Water
½ oz. Triple Sec
½ oz. Curacao
2 oz. Old Mr. Boston Five Star
   Brandy
*Fill pitcher with cubes of ice. Add 1
pint of Sauterne. Stir well and decorate with as many fruits as available
and also rind of cucumber inserted
on each side of pitcher. Top with
small bunch of mint sprigs. Serve in
5 oz. Claret glass.*

Saxon Cocktail

Juice ½ Lime
½ Teaspoon Grenadine
1 ¾ oz. Old Mr. Boston Imported
   Rum
1 Twist Orange Peel
*Shake well with cracked ice and
strain into 3 oz. cocktail glass.*

Sazerac Cocktail

*Put ¼ Teaspoon Absinthe Substitute
into an Old Fashioned cocktail glass
and revolve glass until it is entirely
coated with the Absinthe Substitute.
Then add:*
½ Lump of Sugar
2 Dashes Bitters
*Sufficient water to cover sugar, and
muddle well.*
2 Cubes of Ice
2 oz. Old Mr. Boston Whiskey*
*Stir very well. Add twist of lemon
peel. (For best results, put glass on
ice for a few minutes before using.)*

Scotch Bishop Cocktail

1 oz. Old Mr. Boston Scotch
   Whisky
½ oz. Orange Juice
½ oz. Dry Vermouth
½ Teaspoon Triple Sec
¼ Teaspoon Powdered Sugar
Twist of Lemon Peel
*Shake well with cracked ice and
strain into 3 oz. cocktail glass.*

Scotch Cooler

2 oz. Old Mr. Boston Scotch
   Whisky
3 Dashes Old Mr. Boston Creme de
   Menthe (white)
*Stir into 8 oz. highball glass with ice
cubes. Fill with chilled carbonated
water and stir.*

Scotch Milk Punch

2 oz. Old Mr. Boston Scotch
   Whisky
6 oz. Milk
Teaspoon powdered sugar
*Shake thoroughly with cracked ice.
Pour into 12 oz. Tom Collins glass.
Sprinkle with nutmeg.*

* *Bourbon, Blended, Rye or Canadian.*

Scotch Mist

Fill Old Fashioned cocktail glass with shaved ice. Pour in Old Mr. Boston Scotch Whisky. *Add twist of lemon peel. Serve with short straws.*

Scotch Old Fashioned

Make same as Old Fashioned Cocktail *(See page 68), except substitute* Old Mr. Boston Scotch Whisky.

Scotch Rickey

1 Cube of Ice
Juice ½ Lime
1½ oz. Old Mr. Boston Scotch Whisky
Fill 8 oz. highball glass with carbonated water and stir. Leave lime in glass.

Scotch Sour

1½ oz. Old Mr. Boston Scotch Whisky
Juice of ½ Lime
½ Teaspoon Powdered Sugar
Shake well with cracked ice; strain into 6 oz. sour glass. Decorate with a half-slice of lemon and a cherry.

Scotch Stinger

Same as Stinger Cocktail on page 95, but substitute Old Mr. Boston Scotch Whiskey, *in place of Brandy.*

Scotch Whisky Highball

1 Cube of Ice
2 oz. Old Mr. Boston Scotch Whisky
Fill 8 oz. highball glass with ginger ale or carbonated water. Add twist of lemon peel, if desired, and stir.

Screwdriver

Put 2 or 3 cubes of ice into 6 oz. glass. Add 2 oz. Old Mr. Boston Vodka. *Fill balance of glass with orange juice and stir.*

Sensation Cocktail

Juice of ¼ Lemon
1½ oz. Old Mr. Boston Dry Gin
1 Teaspoon Maraschino
3 Sprigs Fresh Mint
Shake well with cracked ice and strain into 3 oz. cocktail glass.

September Morn Cocktail

White of 1 Egg
1½ oz. Old Mr. Boston Imported Rum
Juice of ½ Lime
1 Teaspoon Grenadine
Shake well with cracked ice and strain into 4 oz. cocktail glass.

Seventh Heaven Cocktail

2 Teaspoons Grapefruit Juice
½ oz. Maraschino
1¼ oz. Old Mr. Boston Dry Gin
Shake well with cracked ice and strain into 3 oz. cocktail glass. Decorate with sprig of fresh mint.

Sevilla Cocktail

½ Teaspoon Powdered Sugar
1 Egg
1 oz. Port Wine
1 oz. Old Mr. Boston Imported Rum
Shake well with cracked ice and strain into 4 oz. cocktail glass.

S

SHAMROCK COCKTAIL

1½ oz. Irish Whiskey
½ oz. Dry Vermouth
1 Teaspoon Old Mr. Boston
    Creme de Menthe (green)
*Stir well with cracked ice and strain
into 3 oz. cocktail glass. Serve with
an olive.*

SHANDY GAFF

5 oz. Beer
5 oz. Ginger Ale
*Use 12 oz. Tom Collins glass and
stir very gently.*

SHANGHAI COCKTAIL

Juice ¼ Lemon
1 Teaspoon Old Mr. Boston
    Anisette
1 oz. Jamaica Rum
½ Teaspoon Grenadine
*Shake well with cracked ice and
strain into 3 oz. cocktail glass.*

SHERRY AND EGG COCKTAIL

*Place an egg in a glass, being care-
ful not to break the yolk. Fill glass
with Sherry. Use 4 oz. cocktail glass.*

SHERRY COBBLER

Dissolve:
1 Teaspoon Powdered Sugar
2 oz. Carbonated Water
Fill goblet with shaved ice; add:
3 oz. Sherry Wine
*Stir well and decorate with fruits in
season. Serve with straws.*

SHERRY COCKTAIL

2½ oz. Sherry Wine
1 Dash Bitters
*Stir well with cracked ice and strain
into 3 oz. cocktail glass. Twist of
orange peel and drop in glass.*

SHERRY EGGNOG

1 Egg
1 Teaspoon Powdered Sugar
3 oz. Sherry Wine
*Fill glass with milk. Shake well with
cracked ice and strain into 12 oz.
Tom Collins glass. Grate nutmeg on
top.*

SHERRY FLIP

1 Egg
1 Teaspoon Powdered Sugar
1½ oz. Sherry Wine
2 Teaspoons Sweet Cream
    (if desired)
*Shake well with cracked ice and
strain into 5 oz. flip glass. Grate a
little nutmeg on top.*

SHERRY MILK PUNCH

1 Teaspoon Powdered Sugar
3 oz. Sherry Wine
½ pt. Milk
*Shake well with cracked ice, strain
into 12 oz. Tom Collins glass and
grate nutmeg on top.*

S

SHERRY SANGAREE

Dissolve ½ teaspoon powdered sugar in 1 teaspoon of water. Add:
2 oz. Sherry Wine
2 cubes of Ice
Serve in 8 oz. highball glass. Fill balance with soda water. Stir, leaving enough room on which to float a tablespoon of Port Wine. Sprinkle lightly with nutmeg.

SHERRY TWIST COCKTAIL

1 oz. Sherry Wine
⅓ oz. Old Mr. Boston Five Star Brandy
⅓ oz. Dry Vermouth
⅓ oz. Triple Sec
½ Teaspoon Lemon Juice
Shake well with cracked ice and strain into 3 oz. cocktail glass. Top with pinch of cinnamon and twist of orange peel dropped in glass.

SHRINER COCKTAIL

1¼ oz. Old Mr. Boston Five Star Brandy
1¼ oz. Old Mr. Boston Sloe Gin
2 Dashes Bitters
½ Teaspoon Simple Syrup
Stir well with cracked ice and strain into 3 oz. cocktail glass. Twist of lemon peel and drop into glass.

SIDECAR COCKTAIL

Juice ¼ Lemon
½ oz. Triple Sec
1 oz. Old Mr. Boston Five Star Brandy
Shake well with cracked ice and strain into 3 oz. cocktail glass.

SILVER COCKTAIL

1 oz. Dry Vermouth
1 oz. Old Mr. Boston Dry Gin
2 Dashes Orange Bitters
¼ Teaspoon Simple Syrup
½ Teaspoon Maraschino
Stir well with cracked ice and strain into 3 oz. cocktail glass. Twist of lemon peel and drop into glass.

SILVER FIZZ

Juice ½ Lemon
1 Teaspoon Powdered Sugar
2 oz. Old Mr. Boston Dry Gin
White of 1 Egg
Shake well with cracked ice and strain into 8 oz. highball glass. Fill with carbonated water and stir.

SILVER KING COCKTAIL

White of 1 Egg
Juice ¼ Lemon
1½ oz. Old Mr. Boston Dry Gin
½ Teaspoon Powdered Sugar
2 Dashes Orange Bitters
Shake well with cracked ice and strain into 4 oz. cocktail glass.

SILVER STALLION FIZZ

1 Scoop Vanilla Ice Cream
2 oz. Old Mr. Boston Dry Gin
Use 8 oz. highball glass; fill with carbonated water and stir.

SINGAPORE SLING

Juice ½ Lemon
1 Teaspoon Powdered Sugar
2 oz. Old Mr. Boston Dry Gin
½ oz. Old Mr. Boston Wild Cherry
    Flavored Brandy
*Shake well with cracked ice and
strain into 12 oz. Tom Collins glass.
Add ice cubes and fill with carbonated water; stir. Decorate with fruits
in season and serve with straws.*

SIR WALTER COCKTAIL

¾ oz. Old Mr. Boston Imported
    Rum
¾ oz. Old Mr. Boston Five Star
    Brandy
1 Teaspoon Grenadine
1 Teaspoon Curacao
1 Teaspoon Lemon Juice
*Shake well with cracked ice and
strain into 3 oz. cocktail glass.*

SLINGS

*See Index on page 146 for complete
list of* SLING *recipes.*

SLOE DRIVER

*Put 2 or 3 cubes of ice into 6 oz. glass
and add:*
2 oz. Old Mr. Boston Sloe Gin
Fill with orange juice and stir.

SLOE GIN COCKTAIL

2 oz. Old Mr. Boston Sloe Gin
1 Dash Orange Bitters
¼ Teaspoon Dry Vermouth
*Stir well with cracked ice and strain
into 3 oz. cocktail glass.*

SLOE GIN COLLINS

Juice ½ Lemon
2 oz. Old Mr. Boston Sloe Gin
*Shake well with cracked ice and
strain into 12 oz. Tom Collins glass.
Add several cubes of ice, fill with carbonated water and stir. Decorate
with slice of lemon, orange and a
cherry. Serve with straws.*

SLOE GIN FIZZ

Juice of ½ Lemon
1 Teaspoon Powdered Sugar
2 oz. Old Mr. Boston Sloe Gin
*Shake well with cracked ice and
strain into 8 oz. highball glass. Fill
with carbonated water and stir. Decorate with slice of lemon.*

SLOE GIN FLIP

1 Egg
1 Teaspoon Powdered Sugar
½ oz. Old Mr. Boston Sloe Gin
2 Teaspoons Sweet Cream
    (if desired)
*Shake well with cracked ice and
strain into 5 oz. flip glass. Grate a
little nutmeg on top.*

SLOE GIN RICKEY

1 Cube of Ice
Juice of ½ Lime
2 oz. Old Mr. Boston Sloe Gin
*Fill 8 oz. highball glass with carbon-
ated water and stir. Leave Lime in
glass.*

SLOEBERRY COCKTAIL

1 Dash Bitters
2 oz. Old Mr. Boston Sloe Gin
*Stir well with cracked ice and strain
into 3 oz. cocktail glass.*

Sloppy Joe's Cocktail No. 1

Juice 1 Lime
¼ Teaspoon Curacao
¼ Teaspoon Grenadine
¾ oz. Old Mr. Boston Imported Rum
¾ oz. Dry Vermouth
Shake well with cracked ice and strain into 3 oz. cocktail glass.

Sloppy Joe's Cocktail No. 2

¾ oz. Pineapple Juice
¾ oz. Old Mr. Boston Five Star Brandy
¾ oz. Port Wine
¼ Teaspoon Curacao
¼ Teaspoon Grenadine
Shake well with cracked ice and strain into 3 oz. cocktail glass.

Smashes

See Index on page 146 for complete list of SMASH recipes.

Smile Cocktail

1 oz. Grenadine
1 oz. Old Mr. Boston Dry Gin
½ Teaspoon Lemon Juice
Shake well with cracked ice and strain into 3 oz. cocktail glass.

Smiler Cocktail

½ oz. Sweet Vermouth
½ oz. Dry Vermouth
1 oz. Old Mr. Boston Dry Gin
1 Dash Bitters
¼ Teaspoon Orange Juice
Shake well with cracked ice and strain into 3 oz. cocktail glass.

Snowball Cocktail

1½ oz. Old Mr. Boston Dry Gin
½ oz. Old Mr. Boston Anisette
½ oz. Sweet Cream
Shake well with cracked ice and strain into 4 oz. cocktail glass.

Society Cocktail

1½ oz. Old Mr. Boston Dry Gin
¾ oz. Dry Vermouth
¼ Teaspoon Grenadine
Stir well with cracked ice and strain into 3 oz. cocktail glass.

Soother Cocktail

½ oz. Old Mr. Boston Five Star Brandy
½ oz. Apple Brandy
½ oz. Curacao
Juice ½ Lemon
1 Teaspoon Powdered Sugar
Shake well with cracked ice and strain into 3 oz. cocktail glass.

Soul Kiss Cocktail

¼ oz. Orange Juice
¼ oz. Dubonnet
¾ oz. Dry Vermouth
¾ oz. Old Mr. Boston Whiskey*
Shake well with cracked ice and strain into 3 oz. cocktail glass.

Sours

See Index on page 146 for complete list of SOUR recipes.

Sourteq

See TEQUILA SOUR on page 97.

* Bourbon, Blended, Rye or Canadian

SOUTH SIDE COCKTAIL

Juice ½ Lemon
1 Teaspoon Powdered Sugar
2 Sprigs Fresh Mint
1½ oz. Old Mr. Boston Dry Gin
Shake well with cracked ice and strain into 3 oz. cocktail glass.

SOUTH SIDE FIZZ

Juice ½ Lemon
1 Teaspoon Powdered Sugar
2 oz. Old Mr. Boston Dry Gin
Shake well with cracked ice and strain into 7 oz. highball glass. Fill with carbonated water and stir. Add fresh mint leaves.

SOUTHERN GIN COCKTAIL

2 oz. Old Mr. Boston Dry Gin
2 Dashes Orange Bitters
½ Teaspoon Curacao
Stir well with cracked ice and strain into 3 oz. cocktail glass. Twist of lemon peel and drop into glass.

SPANISH TOWN COCKTAIL

2 oz. Old Mr. Boston Imported Rum
1 Teaspoon Curacao
Stir well with cracked ice and strain into 3 oz. cocktail glass.

SPECIAL ROUGH COCKTAIL

1¼ oz. Apple Brandy
1¼ oz. Old Mr. Boston Five Star Brandy
¼ Teaspoon Absinthe Substitute
Stir well with cracked ice and strain into 3 oz. cocktail glass.

SPENCER COCKTAIL

¾ oz. Old Mr. Boston Apricot Flavored Brandy
1½ oz. Old Mr. Boston Dry Gin
1 Dash Bitters
¼ Teaspoon Orange Juice
Shake well with cracked ice and strain into 3 oz. cocktail glass. Add a cherry and twist of orange peel.

SPHINX COCKTAIL

1½ oz. Old Mr. Boston Dry Gin
¼ oz. Sweet Vermouth
¼ oz. Dry Vermouth
Stir well with cracked ice and strain into 3 oz. cocktail glass. Serve with slice of lemon on top.

SPRING FEELING COCKTAIL

½ oz. Lemon Juice
½ oz. Green Chartreuse
1 oz. Old Mr. Boston Dry Gin
Shake well with cracked ice and strain into 3 oz. cocktail glass.

SPRITZER HIGHBALL

Pour 3 oz. chilled Rhine Wine or Sauterne into 8 oz. highball glass with ice cubes. Fill balance with carbonated water and stir gently.

STANLEY COCKTAIL

Juice ¼ Lemon
1 Teaspoon Grenadine
¾ oz. Old Mr. Boston Dry Gin
¾ oz. Old Mr. Boston Imported Rum
Shake well with cracked ice and strain into 3 oz. cocktail glass.

STAR COCKTAIL

1 oz. Apple Brandy
1 oz. Sweet Vermouth
1 Dash Bitters
Stir well with cracked ice and strain into 3 oz. cocktail glass. Twist of lemon peel and drop into glass.

STAR DAISY

Juice ½ Lemon
½ Teaspoon Powdered Sugar
1 Teaspoon Raspberry Syrup or
    Grenadine
1 oz. Old Mr. Boston Dry Gin
1 oz. Apple Brandy
Shake well with cracked ice and strain into stein or 8 oz. metal cup. Add cube of ice and decorate with fruit.

STARS AND STRIPES

⅓ Grenadine
⅓ Heavy Sweet Cream
⅓ Creme de Yvette
Pour carefully, in order given, into Pousse Café glass, so that each ingredient floats on preceding one.

STINGER COCKTAIL

1 oz. Old Mr. Boston Creme de
    Menthe (white)
1 oz. Old Mr. Boston Five Star
    Brandy
Shake well with cracked ice and strain into 3 oz. cocktail glass.

STONE COCKTAIL

½ oz. Old Mr. Boston Imported
    Rum
½ oz. Sweet Vermouth
1 oz. Sherry Wine
Stir well with cracked ice and strain into 3 oz. cocktail glass.

STONE FENCE

1 Cube of Ice
2 Dashes Bitters
2 oz. Old Mr. Boston Scotch
    Whisky
Use 8 oz. highball glass and fill with carbonated water or cider and stir.

STRAIGHT LAW COCKTAIL

¾ oz. Old Mr. Boston Dry Gin
1½ oz. Sherry Wine
Stir well with cracked ice and strain into 3 oz. cocktail glass.

SUISSESSE COCKTAIL

1½ oz. Absinthe Substitute
½ oz. Old Mr. Boston Anisette
White of 1 Egg
Shake well with cracked ice and strain into 4 oz. cocktail glass.

SUNSHINE COCKTAIL

¾ oz. Sweet Vermouth
1½ oz. Old Mr. Boston Dry Gin
1 Dash Bitters
Stir well with cracked ice and strain into 3 oz. cocktail glass. Twist of orange peel and drop into glass.

SUSIE TAYLOR

Juice ½ Lime
2 Cubes of Ice
2 oz. Old Mr. Boston Imported
    Rum
Fill 12 oz. Tom Collins glass with ginger ale and stir gently.

SWEET PATOOTIE COCKTAIL

1 oz. Old Mr. Boston Dry Gin
½ oz. Cointreau
½ oz. Orange Juice
Shake well with cracked ice and strain into 3 oz. cocktail glass.

SWISS FAMILY COCKTAIL

½ Teaspoon Absinthe Substitute
2 Dashes Bitters
¾ oz. Dry Vermouth
1½ oz. Old Mr. Boston Whiskey*
Stir well with cracked ice and strain into 3 oz. cocktail glass.

SWIZZLES

See Index on page 147 for complete list of SWIZZLE *recipes.*

TAILSPIN COCKTAIL

¾ oz. Old Mr. Boston Dry Gin
¾ oz. Sweet Vermouth
¾ oz. Green Chartreuse
1 Dash Orange Bitters
Stir well with cracked ice and strain into 3 oz. cocktail glass. Twist of lemon peel and serve with cherry or olive.

TANGO COCKTAIL

½ oz. Orange Juice
½ oz. Dry Vermouth
½ oz. Sweet Vermouth
1 oz. Old Mr. Boston Dry Gin
½ Teaspoon Curacao
Shake well with cracked ice and strain into 4 oz. cocktail glass.

TEMPTATION COCKTAIL

1½ oz. Old Mr. Boston Whiskey*
½ Teaspoon Curacao
½ Teaspoon Absinthe Substitute
½ Teaspoon Dubonnet
1 Twist Orange Peel
1 Twist Lemon Peel
Shake well with cracked ice and strain into 3 oz. cocktail glass.

TEMPTER COCKTAIL

1 oz. Port Wine
1 oz. Old Mr. Boston Apricot
  Flavored Brandy
Stir well with cracked ice and strain into 3 oz. cocktail glass.

* *Bourbon, Blended, Rye or Canadian*

TEQUILA COLLINS

Same as TOM COLLINS *(see page 100) except use Tequila instead of Dry Gin.*

TEQUILA SOUR

Juice ½ Lemon
Teaspoon Powdered Sugar
2 oz. Tequila
Shake well with cracked ice and strain into 6 oz. sour glass. Decorate with a half-slice of lemon and a cherry.

TEQUILA STRAIGHT

⅓ Lemon
Pinch of Salt
Jigger Tequila
First suck lemon, place salt on tongue, then swallow Tequila.

TEQUINI COCKTAIL

1½ oz. Tequila
½ oz. Dry Vermouth
1 Dash Bitters may be added
Stir well with cracked ice and strain into 3 oz. cocktail glass. Serve with twist of lemon peel and an olive.

TEQUONIC

2 oz. Tequila
Juice of ½ Lemon or Lime
Pour Tequila over ice cubes in Old Fashioned cocktail glass. Add fruit juice; fill with tonic water and stir.

THANKSGIVING SPECIAL COCKTAIL

¾ oz. Old Mr. Boston Apricot
    Flavored Brandy
¾ oz. Old Mr. Boston Dry Gin
¾ oz. Dry Vermouth
¼ Teaspoon Lemon Juice
Shake well with cracked ice and strain into 3 oz. cocktail glass. Serve with a cherry.

THIRD DEGREE COCKTAIL

1½ oz. Old Mr. Boston Dry Gin
¾ oz. Dry Vermouth
1 Teaspoon Absinthe Substitute
Stir well with cracked ice and strain into 3 oz. cocktail glass.

THIRD RAIL COCKTAIL

¾ oz. Old Mr. Boston Imported
    Rum
¾ oz. Apple Brandy
¾ oz. Old Mr. Boston Five Star
    Brandy
¼ Teaspoon Absinthe Substitute
Stir well with cracked ice and strain into 3 oz. cocktail glass.

THISTLE COCKTAIL

1¼ oz. Sweet Vermouth
1¼ oz. Old Mr. Boston Scotch
    Whisky
2 Dashes Bitters
Stir well with cracked ice and strain into 3 oz. cocktail glass.

THREE MILLER COCKTAIL

1¼ oz. Old Mr. Boston Imported
    Rum
¾ oz. Old Mr. Boston Five Star
    Brandy
1 Teaspoon Grenadine
¼ Teaspoon Lemon Juice
*Shake well with cracked ice and
strain into 3 oz. cocktail glass.*

THREE STRIPES COCKTAIL

1 oz. Old Mr. Boston Dry Gin
½ oz. Dry Vermouth
½ oz. Orange Juice
*Shake well with cracked ice and
strain into 3 oz. cocktail glass.*

THUNDER COCKTAIL

1 Teaspoon Powdered Sugar
Yolk of 1 Egg
1½ oz. Old Mr. Boston Five Star
    Brandy
1 Pinch of Cayenne Pepper
*Shake well with cracked ice and
strain into 4 oz. cocktail glass.*

THUNDER AND LIGHTNING
COCKTAIL

Yolk of 1 Egg
1 Teaspoon Powdered Sugar
1½ oz. Old Mr. Boston Five Star
    Brandy
*Shake well with cracked ice and
strain into 4 oz. cocktail glass.*

THUNDERCLAP COCKTAIL

¼ oz. Old Mr. Boston Dry Gin
¼ oz. Old Mr. Boston Whiskey*
¼ oz. Old Mr. Boston Five Star
    Brandy
*Stir well with cracked ice and strain
into 3 oz. cocktail glass.*

Bourbon, Blended, Rye or Canadian.

Ginger Flavored Brandy 70 Proof ▶
Flavored Brandy (Blackberry, Peach,
Apricot and Cherry) 70 Proof

T

TIPPERARY COCKTAIL

¾ oz. Irish Whiskey
¾ oz. Green Chartreuse
¾ oz. Sweet Vermouth
*Stir well with cracked ice and strain
into 3 oz. cocktail glass.*

T. N. T. COCKTAIL

1¼ oz. Old Mr. Boston Whiskey*
1¼ oz. Absinthe Substitute
*Stir well with cracked ice and strain
into 3 oz. cocktail glass.*

TODDIES

*See Index on page 147 for complete
list of* TODDY *recipes.*

TOM AND JERRY

*First prepare batter, using mixing
bowl. Separate the yolk and white of
1 egg, beating each separately and
thoroughly. Then combine both, adding enough superfine powdered sugar
to stiffen. Add to this 1 pinch of baking soda and ¼ oz. Old Mr. Boston
Imported Rum to preserve the batter.
Then add a little more sugar to
stiffen. To serve, use hot Tom and
Jerry mug, using 1 tablespoon of
above batter, dissolved in 3 table-
spoons hot milk. Add 1½ oz. Old
Mr. Boston Imported Rum. Then
fill mug with hot milk within ¼ inch
of top of mug and stir gently. Then
top with ½ oz. Old Mr. Boston Five
Star Brandy and grate a little nutmeg on top.*
*The secret of a Tom and Jerry is to
have a stiff batter and a warm mug.*

TOM COLLINS

Juice of ½ Lemon
1 Teaspoon Powdered Sugar
2 oz. Old Mr. Boston Dry Gin
*Shake well with cracked ice an
strain into 12 oz. Tom Collins glas
Add several cubes of ice, fill wit
carbonated water and stir. Decora
with slice of lemon, orange and
cherry. Serve with straws.*

TOVARICH COCKTAIL

1½ oz. Old Mr. Boston Vodka
¾ oz. Old Mr. Boston Kummel
Juice of ½ Lime
*Shake well with cracked ice an
strain into 3 oz. cocktail glass.*

TRILBY COCKTAIL

1½ oz. Old Mr. Boston Whiskey*
¾ oz. Sweet Vermouth
2 Dashes Orange Bitters
*Stir well with cracked ice and strai
into 3 oz. cocktail glass.*

TRINITY COCKTAIL

¾ oz. Sweet Vermouth
¾ oz. Dry Vermouth
¾ oz. Old Mr. Boston Dry Gin
*Stir well with cracked ice and strai
into 3 oz. cocktail glass.*

TROPICAL COCKTAIL

¾ oz. Old Mr. Boston Creme de
    Cacao
¾ oz. Maraschino
¾ oz. Dry Vermouth
1 Dash Bitters
*Stir well with cracked ice and strai
into 3 oz. cocktail glass.*

* *Bourbon, Blended, Rye or Canadia*

Tulip Cocktail

¼ oz. Lemon Juice
¼ oz. Old Mr. Boston Apricot
    Flavored Brandy
¾ oz. Sweet Vermouth
¾ oz. Apple Brandy
Shake well with cracked ice and strain into 3 oz. cocktail glass.

Turf Cocktail

¼ Teaspoon Absinthe Substitute
2 Dashes Bitters
1 oz. Dry Vermouth
1 oz. Old Mr. Boston Dry Gin
Stir well with cracked ice and strain into 3 oz. cocktail glass. Twist of orange peel and drop in glass.

Tuxedo Cocktail

1¼ oz. Old Mr. Boston Dry Gin
1¼ oz. Dry Vermouth
¼ Teaspoon Maraschino
¼ Teaspoon Absinthe Substitute
2 Dashes Orange Bitters
Stir well with cracked ice and strain into 3 oz. cocktail glass. Serve with a cherry.

Twin Six Cocktail

1 oz. Old Mr. Boston Dry Gin
½ oz. Sweet Vermouth
¼ Teaspoon Grenadine
½ oz. Orange Juice
White of 1 Egg
Shake well with cracked ice and strain into 4 oz. cocktail glass.

Twister

2 oz. Old Mr. Boston Vodka
Juice of ⅓ Lime
Pour into 12 oz. Tom Collins glass. Add several cubes of ice, drop rind into glass. Fill with Seven-Up and stir well.

Ulanda Cocktail

1½ oz. Old Mr. Boston Dry Gin
¾ oz. Triple Sec
¼ Teaspoon Absinthe Substitute
Stir well with cracked ice and strain into 3 oz. cocktail glass.

Union Jack Cocktail

¾ oz. Creme de Yvette
1½ oz. Old Mr. Boston Dry Gin
½ Teaspoon Grenadine
Shake well with cracked ice and strain into 3 oz. cocktail glass.

VALENCIA COCKTAIL

½ oz. Orange Juice
1½ oz. Old Mr. Boston Apricot
Flavored Brandy
2 Dashes Orange Bitters
Shake well with cracked ice and strain into 3 oz. cocktail glass.

VANDERBILT COCKTAIL

¾ oz. Old Mr. Boston Wild Cherry
Flavored Brandy
1½ oz. Old Mr. Boston Five Star
Brandy
1 Teaspoon Simple Syrup
2 Dashes Bitters
Stir well with cracked ice and strain into 3 oz. cocktail glass.

VERMOUTH CASSIS

¾ oz. Creme de Cassis
1½ oz. Dry Vermouth
1 Cube of Ice
Fill 8 oz. highball glass with carbonated water and stir.

VERMOUTH COCKTAIL

1 oz. Dry Vermouth
1 oz. Sweet Vermouth
1 Dash Orange Bitters
Stir well with cracked ice and strain into 3 oz. cocktail glass. Serve with a cherry.

VIOLET FIZZ

Juice ½ Lemon
½ Teaspoon Powdered Sugar
1½ oz. Old Mr. Boston Dry Gin
½ oz. Creme de Yvette
Shake well with cracked ice and strain into 7 oz. highball glass. Fill with carbonated water and stir.

VODKA AND APPLE JUICE

Put 2 or 3 cubes of ice into 6 oz. glass. Add 2 oz. Old Mr. Boston Vodka. Fill balance of glass with apple juice and stir.

VODKA AND TONIC

2 oz. Old Mr. Boston Vodka
Cube of Ice
Use 12 oz. Tom Collins glass and fill balance with quinine tonic and stir.

VODKA BLOODY MARY COCKTAIL

See BLOODY MARY COCKTAIL *on page 10.*

VODKA COLLINS

Same as TOM COLLINS *(see page 100) except use* Old Mr. Boston *Vodka instead of dry gin.*

◄ (Cordials) Creme de Cacao 54 Proof White and Brown
Creme de Menthe 60 Proof White and Green
Kummel 70 Proof
Anisette 60 Proof

Vodka Cooler

Same as Gin Cooler *(see page 40),* except use Old Mr. Boston Vodka instead of gin.

Vodka Daisy

Juice ½ Lemon
½ Teaspoon Powdered Sugar
1 Teaspoon Grenadine
2 oz. Old Mr. Boston Vodka
Shake well with cracked ice and strain into stein or 8 oz. metal cup. Add cube of ice and decorate with fruit.

Vodka Gibson Cocktail

See Gibson Cocktail *on page 117.*

Vodka Gimlet Cocktail

Same as Gimlet Cocktail *(see page 40), except use* Old Mr. Boston Vodka *instead of gin.*

Vodka Grasshopper Cocktail

¾ oz. Old Mr. Boston Vodka
¾ oz. Old Mr. Boston Creme de Menthe (green)
¾ oz. Old Mr. Boston Creme de Cacao (white)
Shake well with cracked ice, strain into 3 oz. cocktail glass.

Vodka Gypsy Cocktail

1½ oz. Old Mr. Boston Vodka
¾ oz. Benedictine
1 Dash Bitters
Stir well with cracked ice and strain into 3 oz. cocktail glass.

Vodka Martini Cocktail

See *Special Martini Section* on pages 116 and 117.

Vodka on the Rocks

Put 2 or 3 ice cubes in Old Fashioned glass and add 2 oz. Old Mr. Boston Vodka. *Serve with a twist of lemon peel.*

Vodka "7"

2 oz. Old Mr. Boston Vodka
Juice ½ Lime
Use 12 oz. Tom Collins glass with cubes of ice. Drop lime in glass, fill balance with 7-Up and stir.

Vodka Sling

Same as Gin Sling *(See page 42); except use* Old Mr. Boston Vodka *instead of gin.*

Vodka Sour

Juice ½ Lemon
½ Teaspoon Powdered Sugar
2 oz. Old Mr. Boston Vodka
Shake well with cracked ice and strain into 6 oz. sour glass. Decorate with half-slice of lemon and a cherry.

Vodka Stinger

1 oz. Old Mr. Boston Vodka
1 oz. Old Mr. Boston Creme de Menthe (white)
Shake well with cracked ice and strain into 3 oz. cocktail glass.

Vodkatini

Same as Vodka Martini.

WALLICK COCKTAIL

1¼ oz. Dry Vermouth
1¼ oz. Old Mr. Boston Dry Gin
1 Teaspoon Curacao
*Stir well with cracked ice and strain
into 3 oz. cocktail glass.*

WARD EIGHT

Juice ½ Lemon
1 Teaspoon Powdered Sugar
1 Teaspoon Grenadine
2 oz. Old Mr. Boston Whiskey*
*Shake well with cracked ice and
strain into 8 oz. stem glass previously
prepared with 2 cubes of ice, slice of
orange, lemon and a cherry. Serve
with straws.*

WASHINGTON COCKTAIL

1½ oz. Dry Vermouth
¾ oz. Old Mr. Boston Five Star
   Brandy
2 Dashes Bitters
½ Teaspoon Simple Syrup
*Stir well with cracked ice and strain
into 3 oz. cocktail glass.*

WATERBURY COCKTAIL

½ Teaspoon Powdered Sugar
Juice of ¼ Lemon or ½ Lime
White of 1 Egg
1½ oz. Old Mr. Boston Five Star
   Brandy
½ Teaspoon Grenadine
*Shake well with cracked ice and
strain into 4 oz. cocktail glass.*

WEBSTER COCKTAIL

Juice ½ Lime
¼ oz. Old Mr. Boston Apricot Flavored Brandy
½ oz. Dry Vermouth
1 oz. Old Mr. Boston Dry Gin
*Shake well with cracked ice and
strain into 3 oz. cocktail glass.*

WEDDING BELLE COCKTAIL

¼ oz. Orange Juice
¼ oz. Old Mr. Boston Wild Cherry
   Flavored Brandy
¾ oz. Old Mr. Boston Dry Gin
¾ oz. Dubonnet
*Shake well with cracked ice and
strain into 3 oz. cocktail glass.*

* *Bourbon, Blended, Rye or Canadian.*

W

WEEP NO MORE COCKTAIL

Juice ½ Lime
¾ oz. Dubonnet
¾ oz. Old Mr. Boston Five Star
  Brandy
¼ Teaspoon Maraschino
*Shake well with cracked ice and
strain into 3 oz. cocktail glass.*

WEMBLEY COCKTAIL

¾ oz. Dry Vermouth
1½ oz. Old Mr. Boston Dry Gin
¼ Teaspoon Old Mr. Boston
  Apricot Flavored Brandy
½ Teaspoon Apple Brandy
*Stir well with cracked ice and strain
into 3 oz. cocktail glass.*

WEST INDIES FROSTED
COCKTAIL

See FROZEN DAIQUIRI COCKTAIL *on
page 39.*

WESTERN ROSE COCKTAIL

½ oz. Old Mr. Boston Apricot Flavored Brandy
1 oz. Old Mr. Boston Dry Gin
½ oz. Dry Vermouth
¼ Teaspoon Lemon Juice
*Shake well with cracked ice and
strain into 3 oz. cocktail glass.*

WHIP COCKTAIL

½ oz. Dry Vermouth
½ oz. Sweet Vermouth
1¼ oz. Old Mr. Boston Five Star
  Brandy
¼ Teaspoon Absinthe Substitute
1 Teaspoon Curacao
*Stir well with cracked ice and strain
into 3 oz. cocktail glass.*

WHISKEY COBBLER

Dissolve, in 10 oz. goblet,
1 Teaspoon Powdered Sugar
2 oz. Carbonated Water
Fill goblet with shaved ice; add:
2 oz. Old Mr. Boston Whiskey*
*Stir well and decorate with fruits in
season. Serve with straws.*

WHISKEY COCKTAIL

1 Dash Bitters
1 Teaspoon Simple Syrup
2 oz. Old Mr. Boston Whiskey*
*Stir well with cracked ice and strain
into 3 oz. cocktail glass. Serve with a
cherry.*

WHISKEY COLLINS

Juice of ½ Lemon
1 Teaspoon Powdered Sugar
2 oz. Old Mr. Boston Whiskey*
*Shake well with cracked ice and
strain into 12 oz. Tom Collins glass.
Add several cubes of ice, fill with carbonated water and stir. Decorate
with slice of lemon, orange and a
cherry. Serve with straws.*

WHISKEY DAISY

Juice of ½ Lemon
½ Teaspoon Powdered Sugar
·1 Teaspoon Raspberry Syrup or
  Grenadine
2 oz. Old Mr. Boston Whiskey*
*Shake well with cracked ice and
strain into stein or 8 oz. metal cup.
Add cube of ice and decorate with
fruit.*

* Bourbon, Blended, Rye or Canadian.

WHISKEY EGGNOG

1 Egg
1 Teaspoon Powdered Sugar
2 oz. Old Mr. Boston Whiskey*
Fill glass with Milk. Shake well with cracked ice and strain into 12 oz. Tom Collins glass. Grate nutmeg on top.

WHISKEY FIX

Juice of ½ Lemon
1 Teaspoon Powdered Sugar
1 Teaspoon Water and stir
Fill glass with Shaved Ice
2½ oz. Old Mr. Boston Whiskey*
Use 8 oz. highball glass. Stir well. Add slice of lemon. Serve with straws.

WHISKEY FLIP

1 Egg
1 Teaspoon Powdered Sugar
1½ oz. Old Mr. Boston Whiskey*
2 Teaspoons Sweet Cream (if desired)
Shake well with cracked ice and strain into 5 oz. flip glass. Grate a little nutmeg on top.

WHISKEY HIGHBALL

1 Cube of Ice
2 oz. Old Mr. Boston Whiskey*
Fill 8 oz. highball glass with ginger ale or carbonated water. Add twist of lemon peel, if desired, and stir.

* *Bourbon, Blended, Rye or Canadian.*

Old Mr. Boston Eggnog 30 Proof ▶

WHISKEY MILK PUNCH

1 Teaspoon Powdered Sugar
2 oz. Old Mr. Boston Whiskey*
½ pt. Milk
Shake well with cracked ice, strain into 12 oz. Tom Collins glass and grate nutmeg on top.

WHISKEY ORANGE

Juice of ½ Orange
1 Teaspoon Powdered Sugar
½ Teaspoon Absinthe Substitute
1½ oz. Old Mr. Boston Whiskey*
Shake well with cracked ice and strain into 8 oz. highball glass. Decorate with slice of orange and lemon.

WHISKEY RICKEY

1 Cube of Ice
Juice of ½ Lime
1½ oz. Old Mr. Boston Whiskey*
Fill 8 oz. highball glass with carbonated water and stir. Leave lime in glass.

WHISKEY SANGAREE

Dissolve ½ teaspoon powdered sugar in 1 teaspoon of water. Add:
2 oz. Old Mr. Boston Whiskey*
2 cubes of Ice.
Serve in 8 oz. highball glass. Fill balance with soda water. Stir, leaving enough room on which to float a tablespoon of Port Wine. Sprinkle lightly with nutmeg.

WHISKEY SKIN

Put lump of sugar into hot whiskey glass and fill two-thirds with boiling water. Add 2 oz. Old Mr. Boston Whiskey. Stir, then add twist of lemon peel and drop in glass.*

WHISKEY SLING

Dissolve 1 teaspoon powdered sugar in teaspoon of water and juice ½ lemon
2 oz. Old Mr. Boston Whiskey*
2 Cubes of Ice
Serve in Old Fashioned cocktail glass and stir. Twist of lemon peel and drop in glass.

WHISKEY SMASH

Muddle 1 lump of sugar with
1 oz. Carbonated Water and
4 Sprigs of Green Mint
Add 2 oz. Old Mr. Boston Whiskey,* then a Cube of Ice
Stir and decorate with a slice of orange and a cherry. Twist of lemon peel. Use Old Fashioned cocktail glass.

WHISKEY SOUR

Juice of ½ Lemon
½ Teaspoon Powdered Sugar
2 oz. Old Mr. Boston Whiskey*
Shake well with cracked ice and strain into 6 oz. sour glass. Decorate with a half-slice of lemon and a cherry.

WHISKEY SQUIRT

1½ oz. Old Mr. Boston Whiskey*
1 Tablespoon Powdered Sugar
1 Tablespoon Raspberry Syrup or Grenadine
Shake well with cracked ice and strain into 8 oz. highball glass and fill with carbonated water. Decorate with cubes of pineapple and strawberries.

* *Bourbon, Blended, Rye or Canadian*

Whiskey Swizzle

Made same as Gin Swizzle *(see page 43), using* 2 oz. Old Mr. Boston Whiskey* instead of gin.

Whiskey Toddy

Use Old Fashioned cocktail glass.
½ Teaspoon Powdered Sugar
2 Teaspoons Water
2 oz. Old Mr. Boston Whiskey*
1 Lump of Ice
Stir well. Twist lemon peel and drop in glass.

Whiskey Toddy (Hot)

Put lump of sugar into hot whiskey glass and fill two-thirds with boiling water. Add 2 oz. Old Mr. Boston Whiskey.* *Stir and decorate with slice of lemon. Grate nutmeg on top.*

Whispers of the Frost Cocktail

¾ oz. Old Mr. Boston Whiskey*
¾ oz. Sherry Wine
¾ oz. Port Wine
1 Teaspoon Powdered Sugar
Shake well with cracked ice and strain into 3 oz. cocktail glass. Serve with slices of lemon and orange.

White Cargo Cocktail

1 Small Scoop Vanilla Ice Cream
1 oz. Old Mr. Boston Dry Gin
Shake until thoroughly mixed and add water or Sauterne if the mixture is too thick. Serve in 4 oz. cocktail glass.

White Lady Cocktail

White of 1 Egg
1 Teaspoon Powdered Sugar
1 Teaspoon Sweet Cream
1½ oz. Old Mr. Boston Dry Gin
Shake well with cracked ice and strain into 4 oz. cocktail glass.

White Lily Cocktail

¾ oz. Triple Sec
¾ oz. Old Mr. Boston Imported Rum
¾ oz. Old Mr. Boston Dry Gin
¼ Teaspoon Old Mr. Boston Anisette
Shake well with cracked ice and strain into 3 oz. cocktail glass.

White Lion Cocktail

Juice ½ Lemon
1 Teaspoon Powdered Sugar
2 Dashes Bitters
½ Teaspoon Grenadine
1½ oz. Old Mr. Boston Imported Rum
Shake well with cracked ice and strain into 3 oz. cocktail glass.

White Plush

Pour 2 oz. Old Mr. Boston Whiskey* *into Delmonico glass. Fill balance with milk and drink without stirring.*

White Rose Cocktail

¾ oz. Old Mr. Boston Dry Gin
½ oz. Orange Juice
Juice 1 Lime
½ oz. Maraschino
White of 1 Egg
Shake well with cracked ice and strain into 4 oz. cocktail glass.

---

* *Bourbon, Blended, Rye or Canadian.*

White Way Cocktail

¾ oz. Old Mr. Boston Creme de
Menthe (white)
1½ oz. Old Mr. Boston Dry Gin
*Shake well with cracked ice and
strain into 3 oz. cocktail glass.*

Widow's Kiss Cocktail

½ oz. Yellow Chartreuse
½ oz. Benedictine
1 oz. Apple Brandy
1 Dash Bitters
*Shake well with cracked ice and
strain into 3 oz. cocktail glass.
Strawberry may be served on top.*

Widow's Dream Cocktail

1½ oz. Benedictine
1 Whole Egg
*Shake well with cracked ice and
strain into 4 oz. cocktail glass. Float
1 teaspoon of cream on top.*

Windy Corner Cocktail

2 oz. Old Mr. Boston Blackberry
Flavored Brandy
*Stir well with cracked ice and strain
into 3 oz. cocktail glass. Grate a little
nutmeg on top.*

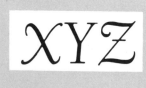

Xanthia Cocktail

¾ oz. Old Mr. Boston Wild Cherry
Flavored Brandy
¾ oz. Yellow Chartreuse
¾ oz. Old Mr. Boston Dry Gin
*Stir well with cracked ice and strain
into 3 oz. cocktail glass.*

X. Y. Z. Cocktail

½ oz. Lemon Juice
½ oz. Triple Sec
1 oz. Old Mr. Boston Imported
Rum
*Shake well with cracked ice and
strain into 3 oz. cocktail glass.*

Xeres Cocktail

1 Dash Orange Bitters
2 oz. Sherry Wine
*Stir well with cracked ice and strain
into 3 oz. cocktail glass.*

Yale Cocktail

1½ oz. Old Mr. Boston Dry Gin
½ oz. Dry Vermouth
1 Dash Bitters
1 Teaspoon Creme de Yvette
*Stir well with cracked ice and strain
into 3 oz. cocktail glass.*

Yellow Parrot Cocktail

¾ oz. Old Mr. Boston Anisette
¾ oz. Yellow Chartreuse
¾ oz. Old Mr. Boston Apricot Flavored Brandy
Stir well with cracked ice and strain into 3 oz. cocktail glass.

Zaza Cocktail

1½ oz. Old Mr. Boston Dry Gin
¾ oz. Dubonnet
1 Twist Orange Peel
Stir well with cracked ice and strain into 3 oz. cocktail glass.

Zero Mint

For each serving desired chill 2 oz. Old Mr. Boston Creme de Menthe (green) mixed with 1 oz. water in freezing compartment of refrigerator for 2 hours or longer if desired. (Does not have to be frozen). Serve in 3 oz. cocktail glasses.

Zombie

1 oz. Unsweetened Pineapple Juice
Juice 1 Lime
Juice 1 Small Orange
1 Teaspoon Powdered Sugar
½ oz. Old Mr. Boston Apricot Flavored Brandy
2½ oz. Old Mr. Boston Imported Rum
1 oz. Jamaica Rum
1 oz. Passion Fruit Juice may be added
Add cracked ice and agitate for full minute in electric mixing machine (if none available, shake very well in cocktail shaker), and strain into 14 oz. frosted zombie glass. Decorate with square of pineapple and 1 green and 1 red cherry.
Carefully float ½ oz. 151 proof Demerara Rum and then top with sprig of fresh Mint dipped in powdered sugar. Serve with straws.

Special Sections

Eggnog

The Martini

Bar Hints and Suggestions

The Liquor Dictionary

Eggnog

SOME PEOPLE BELIEVE that this name is of English derivation and that "nog" comes from the word "noggin," a small drinking vessel with an upright handle. On the other hand, there are those who believe that the name is a result of joining the sounds of egg 'n grog. From whatever source, the drink itself is American dating back to about 1775. In the early days, eggnog was associated with traveling and social functions. Today it is principally associated with Easter, Thanksgiving, Christmas and New Years.

Traditionally, the liquors used in eggnog have been rum and brandy. However, whiskey, sherry, ale and cider may be used. Some of the early recipes called for milking the cow into the liquor but today, fortunately, this is unnecessary as simpler methods are now available. There are excellent nonalcoholic, prepared eggnogs to which one's favorite liquor may be added. These are available during the holiday season from virtually all dairy companies. Most of the following are simplified versions of recipes listed alphabetically in this book (for those who prefer to make their own preparations). For a complete list of recipes see the Index, page 143.

MIXING INSTRUCTIONS

A smaller or greater quantity of liquor than that called for in the following recipes may be used, depending on one's preference. Best results are obtained when all ingredients have been prechilled. Stir well, sprinkle nutmeg on top and serve in 4 oz. punch cups or glasses.

Ambassador's Morning Lift

1 qt. Prepared Dairy Eggnog
6 oz. Cognac
3 oz. Jamaica Rum
3 oz. Old Mr. Boston Creme de Cacao

Old Mr. Boston Five Star Brandy *or* Old Mr. Boston Bourbon Whiskey *may be substituted for Cognac.*

Baltimore Eggnog

1 qt. Prepared Dairy Eggnog
5 oz. Old Mr. Boston Five Star Brandy
5 oz. Jamaica Rum
5 oz. Madeira Wine

Brandy Eggnog

1 qt. Prepared Dairy Eggnog
12 oz. Old Mr. Boston Five Star Brandy

Breakfast Eggnog

1 qt. Prepared Dairy Eggnog
10 oz. Old Mr. Boston Apricot Flavored Brandy
2½ oz. Curacao

Christmas Yule Eggnog

1 qt. Prepared Dairy Eggnog
12 oz. Old Mr. Boston Whiskey*
1½ oz. Old Mr. Boston Imported Rum

General Harrison's Eggnog

1 qt. Prepared Dairy Eggnog
24 oz. Sweet Cider

Imperial Eggnog

1 qt. Prepared Dairy Eggnog
10 oz. Old Mr. Boston Five Star Brandy
2 oz. Old Mr. Boston Apricot Flavored Brandy

Nashville Eggnog

1 qt. Prepared Dairy Eggnog
6 oz. Old Mr. Boston Kentucky Bourbon Whiskey
3 oz. Old Mr. Boston Five Star Brandy
3 oz. Jamaica Rum

Port Wine Eggnog

1 qt. Prepared Dairy Eggnog
18 oz. Port Wine

Rum Eggnog

1 qt. Prepared Dairy Eggnog
12 oz. Old Mr. Boston Imported Rum

Sherry Eggnog

1 qt. Prepared Dairy Eggnog
18 oz. Sherry Wine

Whiskey Eggnog

1 qt. Prepared Dairy Eggnog
12 oz. Old Mr. Boston Whiskey*

* Bourbon, Blended, Rye or Canadian

The Martini

THOUGH THE MARTINI is viewed with almost reverent awe as a drink of unique power, it is no more or less powerful than any other drink containing the same amount of alcohol.

The original Martini recipe called for one-half dry gin and one-half dry vermouth. This proportion began to change in the early 1940s to two or three parts dry gin to one part dry vermouth. Today, popular proportions for an Extra Dry Martini range from a 5–to–1 to an 8–to–1 ratio. The greater the proportion of gin to vermouth, the "drier" the Martini.

ARE YOUR MARTINIS TOO STRONG?

Remember, America is nearly the only country in the world that drinks high-proof gin. The British, who perfected gin, and the Canadians prefer their gin at milder, smoother 80 proof.

To make Martinis that are extra dry but not extra strong, use 80 proof gin. The chart below shows how the trend to drier Martinis has increased the alcoholic content of this popular drink from a smooth 76.5 proof to a powerful 84 proof! Today's very dry Martini can be returned to its original, more moderate proof only by using 80 proof gin.

Using Standard 36 Proof Dry Vermouth	With 90 Proof Dry Gin	Or 80 Proof Dry Gin (or Vodka)
3—to—1 (Traditional)	76.5 Proof	69.0 Proof
5—to—1 (Dry)	81.0 Proof	72.6 Proof
8—to—1 (Extra Dry)	84.0 Proof	75.1 Proof

MARTINI MIXING

Chill 3-ounce cocktail glasses to the point of frost. Fill Martini pitcher with cracked (not crushed) ice. Ice should be dry and hard frozen. Measure out the exact ingredients for the number of drinks required, pouring in the dry gin first (gin should "smoke" as it settles over the cold ice), then the Dry Vermouth. Stir briskly until drink is very cold. Strain at once into frosty, stemmed cocktail glasses. For Martinis "on the rocks," use prechilled Old-Fashioned glasses and pour the liquor over cubes of ice. A twist of lemon peel (see page 125) adds a special character to a Martini which many prefer.

The following are the more popular Martinis.

MARTINI (Traditional 2-to-1)
1½ oz. Old Mr. Boston Dry Gin
¾ oz. Dry Vermouth
Serve with an olive

DRY MARTINI (5-to-1)
1⅔ oz. Old Mr. Boston Dry Gin
⅓ oz. Dry Vermouth
Serve with an olive

EXTRA DRY MARTINI (7-to-1)
1¾ oz. Old Mr. Boston Dry Gin
¼ oz. Dry Vermouth
Serve with an olive

MARTINI (Sweet)
1 oz. Old Mr. Boston Dry Gin
1 oz. Sweet Vermouth
Serve with an olive.

VODKA MARTINI—VODKATINI
Substitute Old Mr. Boston Vodka *for* Old Mr. Boston Dry Gin *in any of these Martini recipes.*

MARTINI (Medium)
1½ oz. Old Mr. Boston Dry Gin
½ oz. Dry Vermouth
½ oz. Sweet Vermouth
Serve with an olive

BOSTON BULLET
A Martini substituting an olive stuffed with an almond for the regular olive.

DILLATINI
A Martini substituting a Dilly Bean in place of the olive.

GIBSON
This is a Dry or Extra Dry Martini with a twist of lemon peel and served with one to three pearl onions. May also be made with Old Mr. Boston Vodka.

TEQUINI
A Martini made with Tequila instead of dry gin. Serve with a twist of lemon peel and an olive.

Bar Hints and Measurements

Here are some suggestions and fine points that will help you mix a perfect drink every time. Follow them carefully and your drinks will have the extra added touch of artistry that will mark you as a professional.

EQUIPMENT

Here is a sensible list of basic, serviceable items for even the most professional bar.

A jigger measure—designed with an accurate scale of half and quarter ounces
A sturdy mixing glass or shaker
A bar strainer
A teaspoon or set of measuring spoons
A glass stirring rod, or a long spoon—for mixing and stirring
A corkscrew, can and bottle opener
A paring knife—for paring and cutting fruit
A vacuum-type ice bucket with tongs
A wooden muddler—for mashing mint, herbs, fruits
A lemon-lime squeezer
A large pitcher—with a good pouring lip
A variety of glassware (See inside back cover)

Use the following as a reference for determining approximately how many bottles you may need for various occasions. To be extra safe, but conservative, substitute quarts for fifths.

No. of People	For Cock- tails	You'll Need at Least	For Buffet or Dinner	You'll Need at Least	For an After- Dinner Party	You'll Need at Least
4	10 to 16 drinks	1 fifth	8 cocktails 8 glasses wine 4 liqueurs 8 highballs	1 fifth 2 bottles ⅘ pint 1 fifth	12 to 16 drinks	1 fifth
6	15 to 22 drinks	2 fifths	12 cocktails 12 glasses wine 8 liqueurs 18 highballs	1 fifth 2 bottles 1 fifth 2 fifths	18 to 26 drinks	2 fifths
8	18 to 24 drinks	2 fifths	16 cocktails 16 glasses wine 10 liqueurs 18 highballs	1 fifth 3 bottles 1 fifth 2 fifths	20 to 34 drinks	2 fifths
12	20 to 40 drinks	3 fifths	24 cocktails 24 glasses wine 16 liqueurs 30 highballs	2 fifths 4 bottles 1 fifth 3 fifths	25 to 45 drinks	3 fifths
20	40 to 65 drinks	4 fifths	40 cocktails 40 glasses wine 25 liqueurs 50 highballs	3 fifths 7 bottles 2 fifths 4 fifths	45 to 75 drinks	5 fifths

MEASURING

Even the most professional bartender measures the ingredients of every drink, even though experience may permit some to do this by eye and by skillful freehand pouring. However, to make a perfect drink every time, measure all ingredients. Remember, too, that many drinks can be spoiled by being too strong as well as too weak.

Some standard bar measures:

1 Dash....................	⅙ teaspoon (1/32 ounce)
1 Teaspoon (bar spoon).......	⅛ ounce
1 Pony....................	1 ounce
1 Jigger (barglass)............	1½ ounces
1 Wineglass.................	4 ounces
1 Split....................	6 ounces
1 Cup....................	8 ounces

Some other helpful measures:

1 Miniature (nip).............	1, 1.6 or 2 ounces
1 Half pint (¼ quart).........	8 ounces (1/16 gallon)
1 Tenth (⅘ pint).............	12.8 ounces (1/10 gallon)
1 Pint (½ quart)..............	16 ounces (⅛ gallon)
1 Fifth (⅘ quart).............	25.6 ounces (⅕ gallon)
1 Quart....................	32 ounces (¼ gallon)
1 Imperial Quart.............	38.4 ounces
1 Half gallon................	64 ounces
1 Gallon...................	128 ounces

And some *average* dry wine and champagne bottle measures:

Split (¼ bottle)	6 to 6½	ounces
"Pint" (½ bottle)	11 to 13	ounces
"Quart" (1 bottle)	24 to 26	ounces
Magnum (2 bottles)		52 ounces
Jeroboam (4 bottles)		104 ounces
Tappit-hen		128 ounces
		(1 gallon)
Rehoboam (6 bottles)		156 ounces
		(1.22 gallons)
Methuselah (8 bottles)		208 ounces
		(1.625 gallons)
Salmanazar (12 bottles)		312 ounces
		(2.44 gallons)
Balthazar (16 bottles)		416 ounces
		(3.3 gallons)
Nebuchadnezzar		520 ounces
(20 bottles)		(4.07 gallons)
Demijohn		627.2 ounces
		(4.9 gallons)

GLASSWARE

All recipes in this book indicate the size and type of glass that is appropriate for each drink. For a complete list and illustration of recommended glassware, see the inside back cover.

Always use clean sparkling glassware. Keep one towel for drying and another for polishing. A stemmed glass should be used for cold drinks served without ice, like Martinis. When held, the heat of the hand will not warm the drink as it is being consumed.

HOW TO CHILL A GLASS

Cocktail glasses should be well chilled to keep the drinks refreshingly cold. If refrigerator space is not available for prechilling, fill each glass with cracked, shaved or crushed ice before mixing. When the drink is ready, empty the glass, shake out the melted ice and then pour the drink.

How to Frost a Glass

There are two types of "frosted" glass. For "frosted" drinks, glasses should be stored in a refrigerator or buried in shaved ice long enough to give each glass a white, frosted, ice-cold look and feel.

For a "sugar-frosted" glass, moisten the rim of a prechilled glass with a slice of lime or lemon and then dip the rim into powdered sugar.

Ice

Use plenty of ice. Whether cubed, cracked, crushed or shaved, all ice should be fresh, crystal-clear and free of any taste. Always put ice in the mixing glass, shaker or drinking glass before pouring any ingredients. The liquids are chilled as they are poured over the ice and there is no splashing.

Most highballs, Old Fashioneds and on-the-rocks drinks call for cubed ice. Use cracked or cubed ice for stirring and shaking; crushed or shaved ice for special tall drinks, frappés and other drinks to be sipped through straws.

Sugar

Always place sugar in the mixing glass before adding the liquor. Unless otherwise stated in the recipe, powdered sugar should be used with alcohol. Powdered sugar dissolves and blends quickest with alcohol at low temperatures.

Simple Syrup

Simple syrup may be substituted for powdered sugar in many drinks. Some bartenders claim it gives certain drinks a smoother, richer taste. Many prefer it because it blends instantly. You may make a simple syrup ahead of time and store it in bottles in a cool place. Dissolve one pound of granulated sugar in one half pint of warm water, gradually stirring in enough water to make one pint of syrup.

When to Stir

Drinks containing clear liquors and ingredients require stirring with ice for proper mixing. Stir drinks containing a carbonated mixer (tonic water, ginger ale, cola, etc.) *gently* to preserve the sparkle and effervescence. Remember, too little stirring fails to mix or chill the ingredients; too much stirring melts the ice and dilutes the drink.

When to Shake

Drinks containing fruit juices, sugar, eggs, cream or other ingredients difficult to mix, should be shaken briskly. For thorough blending of some punches, sours, other fruit and egg drinks, and where frothiness is desired, use an electric mixer or blender.

Using the Strainer

Strain all cocktails before serving with a wire—not silver—strainer. Use one with clips that permits the wire to rest within the rim of the mixing glass or shaker.

Pouring

When mixing the same cocktail for four or more people, make the drinks in one batch. To make each drink of equal strength and taste set up the required number of glasses in a row. Pour, filling each glass only halfway. Then go back to the first glass and finish off.

How to Float Cordials

To make cordials or brandy float one on top of the other in the same glass, as in the Pousse Café, pour each ingredient slowly over a teaspoon held bottom side up over the glass. The rounded surface of the teaspoon will spread each cordial or brandy slowly and evenly over the one below without mixing. This may also be accomplished by first inserting a glass stirring rod into the glass and then slowly pouring each ingredient down the rod.

Be sure to pour all ingredients in the order given in the recipe.

How to Flame Liquor

The secret to setting liquor (brandy, rum, gin, whiskey) aflame in drink and cooking recipes is to make certain that glass, cooking vessel and liquor are all prewarmed. Start with a teaspoon or tablespoon of liquor, preheat over flame, then set afire. Pour flaming liquid carefully into remaining liquor to be set aflame.

Using Eggs

To separate the white of an egg from the yellow, break the egg by hitting the center on the edge of a glass. Separate the two halves, passing the yolk from one half-shell to the other until the white slips through to the glass below.

The egg always goes into the mixing glass or shaker before the liquor, to make certain that the egg is fresh. When shaking, use cubed or cracked ice to break up and blend the egg with the other ingredients.

Using Fruit and Fruit Juices

Whenever possible use only *fresh* fruit. Wash the outside peel before using. Fruit slices should be cut about one-quarter-inch thick and slit toward the center to fix slice on rim of glass. Keep garnishes fresh and cold.

When mixing drinks containing fruit juices, *always* pour the liquor last. Squeeze and strain fruit juices just before using to insure freshness and good taste. Avoid artificial, concentrated substitutes.

TWIST OF LEMON PEEL

When recipes call for a twist of lemon peel, rub a narrow strip of peel around the rim of the glass to deposit the oil on it. Then twist the peel so that the oil (usually one small drop) will drop into the drink. Then drop in the peel. The lemon oil gives added character to the cocktail which many prefer.

USING BITTERS

Ordinarily, only a dash or two is necessary. This small but important ingredient can add zest to a great number of mixed drinks. Made from numerous and subtle combinations of roots, barks, berries and herbs, they are all characterized by their aromatic, bitter taste.
Here are a few of the best-known brands:

Angostura Bitters—made in Trinidad from an ancient, secret recipe.

Abbott's Aged Bitters—made in Baltimore by the same family since 1865.

Peychaud's Bitters—made in New Orleans.

Orange Bitters—made from the dried peel of bitter Seville oranges and sold by several English firms.

VERMOUTH

Vermouth is a white appetizer wine flavored with as many as thirty to forty different herbs, roots, berries, flowers and seeds. There are nearly as many vermouth formulas as there are brand labels.

The dry variety (French) is light gold in color and has a delightful nutty flavor. Sweet (Italian) vermouth is richer in flavor and more syrupy. Both are delicate and will lose their freshness if left too long in an opened bottle. Use with care and discretion in mixed drinks (follow the recipe) since most people now prefer "drier" cocktails.

The Liquor Dictionary

Much of the enjoyment of social drinking comes from a knowledge of the different types of alcoholic beverages available. This section was prepared to help you understand some of the, ofttimes subtle, differences between one type of liquor and another.

First, here are a few common terms frequently misunderstood:

ALCOHOL (C_2H_5OH) the common ingredient of all liquor. There are many types of alcohol, but for beverages only ethyl alcohol is used. Of the several types of ethyl alcohol, those spirits distilled from grain, grape, fruit and cane are the most common.

PROOF—a measurement of alcoholic strength or content. One degree of proof equals one-half of 1 per cent of alcohol. An 80 proof product contains 40 per cent alcohol; a 90 proof product, 45 per cent alcohol, etc.

For centuries Scotch, British Gin and Canadian Whisky sold in England, Scotland, Canada and most of the rest of the world has been sold at mild 80 proof. America has only begun to appreciate the tasteful qualities of the more moderate lower proofs.

In recent years, a trend has developed in this country toward 80 proof blended and straight whiskeys, dry gin, Scotch and Canadian whiskies. Practically all of the *Rum* sold in America is now 80 proof. *Vodka* at 80 proof outsells the higher proofs 9-to-1. For years the most expensive, famous-name Cognacs have been imported at 80 proof, and now nearly all American-made *Brandy* is 80 proof.

Age—often believed to be the *only* indication of quality; a whiskey, rum, or brandy can be aged too long as well as not long enough. Other factors affecting quality include variables in the distilling process itself, the types of grain used, the warehousing techniques employed, the rate of aging and the degree of skill used in determining product maturity. Aging may make good whiskey better, but no amount of aging can make good whiskey out of bad.

Grain Neutral Spirits—a practically tasteless, colorless alcohol distilled from grain (like whiskey) but at 190 proof or above, whereas whiskey must be distilled at less than 190 proof. Used in blended whiskeys, in making gin and vodka, and in many other liquors.

Wine—produced principally from the fermented juice of grapes. If any other fruit is used, the name of the fruit must appear on the label. The alcoholic content of wine ranges from less than 14 per cent to 21 per cent.

Beer—the name for five types of fermented malt beverages: *Lager Beer* (about 3.6 per cent alcohol), the most popular type of light, dry beer; *Ale,* having a more pronounced flavor and aroma of hops, is heavier and more bitter than lager beer; *Bock Beer, Porter* and *Stout* (about 6 per cent alcohol), which are progressively heavier, darker, richer and sweeter than either lager beer or ale.

Brandy

BRANDY IS DISTILLED from a fermented mash of grapes or other fruit. These brandies, aged in oak casks, are usually bottled at either 80 or 84 proof. Long enjoyed as an after-dinner drink, brandy is also widely used in cooking.

COGNAC—this fine brandy, known for its smoothness and heady dry aroma, is produced only in the Cognac region of France. (All Cognac is brandy, but not all brandy is Cognac, nor is all French brandy Cognac.)

ARMAGNAC—is much like Cognac but has a drier taste. It is produced only in the Armagnac region of France.

AMERICAN BRANDY—all of which is distilled in California, has its own excellent characteristics of taste. Unlike European brandies (whose farmer-distillers sell their brandies to blender-shippers who control the brand names), California brandies are usually produced by individual firms that grow the grapes, distill, age, blend, bottle and market the brandies under their own brand names.

APPLE BRANDY, APPLE JACK or CALVADOS—is distilled from a cider made from apples. Calvados is produced only in Normandy, France. Apple Jack may be bottled-in-bond under the same regulations that apply to whiskey.

FRUIT-FLAVORED BRANDIES—are brandy-based liqueurs produced from Blackberries, Peaches, Apricots, Cherries and Ginger. They are usually bottled at 70 or 80 proof.

Cordials

THE words Cordial and Liqueur are synonymous, describing liquors made by mixing or redistilling neutral spirits with fruits, flowers, herbs, seeds, roots, plants or juices to which sweetening has been added. Practically all cordials are sweet and colorful, with highly concentrated, dessertlike flavor.

Cordials are made in all countries. Several, made from closely guarded secret recipes and processes, are known throughout the world by their trade or proprietary brand names.

Here are brief descriptions of the cordials and flavorings mentioned most frequently in the recipes in this book:

ABSINTHE—anise seed (licorice) flavor; contains wormwood; illegal in the United States

ABSINTHE SUBSTITUTES—Abisante, Abson, Anisette, Herbsaint, Mistra, Ojen, Oxygene, Pernod

AMER PICON—bitter, orange-flavored French cordial made from quinine and spices

ANISETTE—anise seed, licorice flavor

BENEDICTINE—secret herb formula first produced by Benedictine monks

BITTERS—(see page 125)

CHARTREUSE—yellow and green herb liqueurs developed by Carthusian monks

CREME(S)—so-called because high sugar content results in cream-like consistency

    CREME DE CACAO—from cacao and vanilla beans

    CREME DE CASSIS—from black currants

    CREME DE MENTHE—from mint

    CREME DE YVETTE—from violets

CURACAO—orange-flavored, made of dried orange peel, from Dutch West Indies

DUBONNET—French aperitif wine made from aromatics, has slight quinine taste

GRENADINE—made from pomegranates, used for flavoring

KUMMEL—caraway and anise seeds and other herb flavors

MARASCHINO—liqueur made from cherries grown in Dalmatia, Yugoslavia

PASSION FRUIT (PASSIONOLA)—a nonalcoholic mix made from the Passion Flower

PEPPERMINT SCHNAPPS—a light-bodied creme de menthe

PERNOD—a French anise-flavored liqueur and absinthe substitute

ROCK AND RYE—fruit juice, rock candy and rye whiskey, bottled with fruit slices

SLOE GIN—a liqueur made from sloe berries (blackthorn bush)

SWEDISH PUNCH—Scandinavian liqueur made from Batavia Arak rum, tea, lemon and other spices. Also known as Arrack Punsch and Caloric Punsch (the latter because it gives off heat)

TEQUILA—a colorless Mexican liquor made from the mescal plant. Not to be confused with Pulque, made from the same plant, but with a heavy sour milk flavor.

TRIPLE SEC—colorless Curacao, but less sweet.

Gin

GIN, which is distilled from grain, receives its flavor and aroma from juniper berries and other botanicals. (Every gin producer has his own special recipe.)

Most gin is colorless, though some brands may be golden or straw-yellow because of aging in barrels. Even though a distiller ages his gin, he cannot, by law, make age claims for his product. Gin sold around the world at 80 proof is bottled in this country at proofs varying from 80 to 94.

DRY GIN—merely signifies that the gin lacks sweetness.

VACUUM-DISTILLED DRY GIN—is distilled in a glass-lined vacuum still at a low 90° Fahrenheit temperature (instead of at the usual 212°), capturing only the light, volatile flavors and aromas without the bitterness found in some gins.

LONDON DRY GIN—originated in England and is now considered a generic term and may appear on American-made gins as well. Dry gins from England are inclined to be a little heavier-bodied.

GOLDEN GIN—is a dry gin which, due to aging in wood, has acquired a golden color.

HOLLAND, GENEVA OR SCHIEDAM GINS—are imported from Holland, where gin originated, are highly flavored and rich in aromatic oils; they do not mix well with other ingredients in cocktails.

OLD TOM GIN—is an English gin that has been sweetened with sugar syrup.

FLAVORED GIN—is a sweet gin usually flavored with orange, lemon or mint.

SLOE GIN—is not a gin at all but a liqueur. (See page 130.)

Rum

Rum is distilled from the fermented juice of sugar cane, cane syrup and molasses at less than 190 proof (160 proof for New England rum) and bottled at not less than 80 proof. It is aged in uncharred barrels where it picks up very little coloring; dark rums often have caramel added to them for color .

Most rums are blends of several aged rums, ranging from heavy, pungent types to light, brandylike varieties, selected for special aroma, flavor and color. There are two main types of rum:

LIGHT-BODIED RUMS—are dry with only a very slight molasses flavor. Available in two varieties, White and Gold Label (or Light and Dark), the Gold or Dark is usually a bit sweeter with a more pronounced taste. Among these rums are included rums from Puerto Rico, Cuba and the Virgin Islands. Light-bodied rums are also produced in the Dominican Republic, Haiti, Venezuela, Mexico, Hawaii and the Philippines.

HEAVY-BODIED RUMS—are darker, sweeter and have a pungent bouquet, body and flavor. These are distilled by a different and slower fermentation process, which allows more time for a fuller, richer molasseslike body to develop and include rums from Jamaica, Demerara (British Guiana), Martinique, Trinidad, Barbados and New England.

Vodka

VODKA, most versatile of all alcoholic beverages, is a highly re-
fined and filtered liquor distilled from any material at or above
190 proof, bottled at not less than 80 or more than 110 proof. It
was originally made in Russia, from potatoes; but in the United
States, vodka is usually distilled from grain, primarily corn and
wheat. The subtle differences between various vodkas results
from the types of grain used and the distilling and filtering processes employed. Most American vodkas are filtered through acti-
vated charcoal.

Vodka is not aged; it is colorless and virtually tasteless and
odorless. In Russia and the Baltic countries, vodka is always
taken straight and ice-cold from small glasses, at one swallow,
along with food. In America, vodka is usually mixed with fruit
juices, carbonated beverages and other ingredients where vodka's
softness and palatability does not interfere with the taste of the
main ingredient.

FLAVORED VODKA—an American-originated product. Excellent
straight or in mixed drinks, it has been sweetened and flavored,
usually with orange, lemon, lime, mint or grape. It is usually
bottled at 70 proof.

ZUBROVKA—vodka in which a bit of special "buffalo" grass
is steeped. This European grass gives the vodka a light yellow-
ish color and a slight aromatic bouquet. It can be made at home
by buying "buffalo" grass from an herb company and steeping
it in vodka. Zubrovka is used like Vodka.

Whiskey

W HISKEYS are distilled from a fermented mash of grain (usually corn, rye, barley or wheat), and then aged in oak barrels In this country, whiskey must be distilled at less than 190 proof (although whiskey with a specific designation such as Bourbon, Rye, etc., cannot be distilled above 160 proof) and must be bottled at no less than 80 proof.

Whiskey, when placed in barrels to age, is a water-colored liquid. It is during the aging period that whiskey obtains its characteristic amber color, flavor and aroma.

The major whiskey-producing countries are the United States, Canada, Scotland and Ireland. Special grain characteristics, recipes and distillation processes make the whiskey of each country distinct from that of the others.

AMERICAN WHISKEY—Although American whiskeys fall into two major categories, straight whiskey and blended whiskey, the United States Government acknowledges thirty-three distinct types of whiskey. Only the major types (98 per cent of the nation's consumption) are covered here.

Straight Whiskey is distilled from corn, rye, barley or wheat (not blended with neutral grain spirits or any other whiskey) and aged in charred oak barrels for a minimum of two years. There are four major types of straight whiskey:

1. *Bourbon Whiskey* is distilled from a mash of grain containing not less than 51 per cent corn and is normally aged four years in new charred oak barrels. Bourbon is amber in color and full-bodied in flavor. When distilled in Kentucky it is usually referred to as *Kentucky Straight Bourbon Whiskey*. Bourbon is named for Bourbon County in Kentucky where this type of whiskey originated. Bourbon is also produced in Illinois, Indiana, Ohio, Pennsylvania, Tennessee and Missouri.

2. *Rye Whiskey* is distilled from a mash of grain containing not less than 51 per cent rye and is much like bourbon in color, but it is different in taste and heavier in flavor.

3. *Corn Whiskey* is distilled from a mash of grain containing not less than 80 per cent corn. Corn whiskey is commonly aged in re-used charred oak barrels.

4. *Bottled-in-Bond Whiskey* is straight whiskey, usually bourbon or rye, which is produced under United States Government supervision. Though the government does not guarantee the quality of bonded whiskey, it does require that the whiskey be at least four years old, that it be bottled at 100 proof, that it be produced in one distilling by the same distiller, and that it be stored and bottled at a bonded warehouse under government supervision.

Blended Whiskey—A blend of one or more straight whiskeys and neutral grain spirits containing at least 20 per cent or more straight whiskey bottled at not less than 80 proof.

1. *Kentucky Whiskey—A Blend* is a blended whiskey in which all the straight whiskeys are distilled in Kentucky.

2. *A Blend of Straight Whiskeys* occurs when two or more straight whiskeys are blended together, to the exclusion of neutral grain spirits.

CANADIAN WHISKY—Canadian whiskies are blended whiskies, usually distilled from rye, corn and barley. Produced only in Canada, under government supervision, most of the Canadian whisky sold in this country is at least four years old. Canadian whisky, usually lighter bodied than American whiskey, is sold in Canada, and in most of the world, except the United States, at 80 proof.

SCOTCH WHISKY—Produced only in Scotland, Scotch whiskies are blended whiskies deriving their individual personalities from native barley grain and traditional pot stills. All Scotch blends contain malt whisky and grain whisky (similar to American grain neutral spirits). Scotch's distinctive smoky flavor comes from drying malted barley over peat fires. All the Scotch imported into this country is at least four years old and is usually 80 or 86 proof. Scotch sold in the rest of the world is almost always 80 proof.

IRISH WHISKEY—Produced only in Ireland, Irish whiskey, like Scotch, is a blended whiskey containing both barley malt whiskeys and grain whiskeys. Unlike Scotch, however, the malt is dried in coal-fired kilns and the aroma of the fires does not reach the malt. Irish whiskey is heavier and more full-bodied than Scotch and is usually 86 proof.

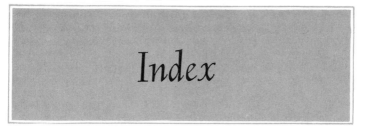

Index

If you know the name of the mixed drink you desire, you need not use this index, as all drinks are listed alphabetically throughout the book.

This index is arranged so that you may choose specific types of drinks such as cocktails, fizzes, highballs, etc., or cocktails made with Vodka, Gin, Whiskey, Sloe Gin and other ingredients.

138

These tall drinks are gener-
ally served in a large goblet.
They are made with lots of
shaved ice, fruit and liquor,
decorated with berries, fresh
fruit and, if desired, a sprig
of mint. Serve with straws.

COLLINS

These are tall, cool drinks be-
longing to the Punch family,
with Tom and John the best
known members. Any basic
liquor can be used, with the
juice of lemon or lime, over
ice cubes in a frosted, 12 oz.
highball glass, with sugar
added to taste and filled with
soda water. Garnish with a
slice of lemon and a cherry.

EGGNOGS

This is a most agreeable, enriching way of taking whole eggs and milk. They can be served in cups, from a bowl, at the holiday season or in a tall, individually prepared glass. In either case, a sprinkling of nutmeg is a must.

FIZZES

An early morning, midafternoon or evening pleasure, these are made from liquor, citrus juices and sugar, shaken with ice and strained into small highball glasses, which are then filled with "fizz" (soda) water, though different carbonated beverages, even Champagne, may be used. A few call for egg whites or yolks.

FLIPS

This combination Eggnog and Fizz is made with liquor, egg and sugar, shaken well with cracked ice and strained into short-stemmed flip glasses. Good early-morning or bedtime drinks, sprinkled with nutmeg.

Pousse Cafés

These sweet, striped wonders are made from a series of cordials and liqueurs poured in succession so that one floats on another. Follow the recipes exactly to get the layers of ingredients in the right order. See "How To Float Cordials" in the Bar Hints section.

Punches

Perfect for parties, they can be mixed in endless variety. Cold punches usually contain citrus juices with two or more liquors or wines. Hot punches often use milk, eggs and cream as a base.

Rickeys

A cross between a Collins and a Sour, they are always made with lime, cracked ice, soda water or some other carbonated beverage. The liquor may be whiskey, gin, rum or brandy. Serve with the rind of the lime left in the glass.

Rum Drinks

(Also see Jamaica Rum Drinks on page 144)

Rye Whiskey Drinks

(See Whiskey Drinks, on page 147 of Index)

Sangarees

These are taller, sweet Old Fashioneds (without bitters); they may be made with whiskey, gin, rum or brandy, with port wine floated on top, or with wine, ale, porter or stout, with a sprinkle of nutmeg.

Scotch Whisky Drinks

Slings

These are like Sangarees, but made with the addition of lemon juice and a twist of lemon peel. Usually served in an Old Fashioned glass.

Sloe Gin Drinks

Smashes

These are junior-sized Juleps served in Old Fashioned glasses. Make with muddled sugar, ice cubes and whiskey, gin, rum or brandy as well as sprigs of mint and a squirt of soda water, if desired, and garnish with fruit.

Sours

Made with lemon juice, ice, sugar and any of the basic liquors, these are tart lemon-y cocktails similar to a highly concentrated Punch. Decorate with a lemon slice and cherry.

Swedish Punch Drinks

SWIZZLES

These drinks originally came from the West Indies where a swizzle stick is a twig having three to five forked branches on the end; it is inserted into the glass or pitcher and twirled rapidly between the hands. Tall, cool drinks of lime, sugar, liquor, bitters and packed with shaved ice.

TEQUILA DRINKS

TODDIES

These may be served hot or cold. Dissolve a lump or teaspoon of sugar in a little water. Add liquor, ice or hot water and stir with clove, nutmeg, cinnamon or lemon peel.

TRIPLE SEC DRINKS

VODKA DRINKS

WHISKEY DRINKS

(Bourbon, Blended,
Rye or Canadian)

148

PRODUCT ILLUSTRATIONS

DECORATE WITH LABELS

In response to many requests, Old Mr. Boston now offers a variety of colorful liquor labels for use in decorating waste baskets, lamp shades, screens, room dividers, trays, table tops, home bars and other such articles. All labels are genuine, have been printed in many colors, some on gold and silver foil paper. Many are embossed and several are die-cut into attractive, interesting shapes.

For a package of 30 different labels, in a variety of sizes, complete with illustrated instructions, send $1.00 to Decorating Labels, Old Mr. Boston, Boston 18, Mass.

PEARL-WHITE POURER

Illustrated on page 46. Safe, practical and washable, they screw on, have no corks to crumble, stick or replace. Interchangeable on all Old Mr. Boston fifths and quarts. 25¢ each from Pourer, Old Mr. Boston, Boston 18, Mass.

Hurting TIME

ANNE SCHRAFF

SADDLEBACK
EDUCATIONAL PUBLISHING

SADDLEBACK
EDUCATIONAL PUBLISHING
www.sdlback.com

© **2012 by Saddleback Educational Publishing**
All rights reserved. No part of this book may be reproduced in any form or by any means, electronic or mechanical, including photocopying, recording, scanning, or by any information storage and retrieval system, without the written permission of the publisher. SADDLEBACK EDUCATIONAL PUBLISHING and any associated logos are trademarks and/or registered trademarks of Saddleback Educational Publishing.

ISBN-13: 978-1-61651-959-9
ISBN-10: 1-61651-959-2
eBook: 978-1-61247-645-2

Printed in Guangzhou, China
0512/CA21200822

16 15 14 13 12 1 2 3 4 5

CHAPTER ONE

Abel!" Liza Ruiz, Abel's mother, cried in an exasperated voice. "*What on earth is wrong with you?* You're doing good in your senior year at school. I see your report cards. You're making money at the dough-nut shop. You're even working part-time at that ritzy seafood place, the Sting Ray, and making money there. You have good friends. You have a family that loves you. Why are you acting like someone on death row waiting to be executed?"

Abel Ruiz continued texting, ignor-ing his mother. At one time in his life, his mother had frightened him. He struggled for her approval. She compared him unfa-vorably with his older brother, Tomás, who

1

was away at college. Tomás was handsome, brilliant, and charming. Abel was none of these. But finally Abel had reached the point of no longer needing his mother's approval.

"Abel!" Sal Ruiz, Abel's father, barked at him. Sal Ruiz was a landscaper, and he also failed to live up to Liza Ruiz's expectations. "Answer your mother," his father said. "She's worried about you. We both are."

"I'm fine," Abel snapped. All through Abel's life, his home life was the same. Mom was the boss. She ruled everyone—Tomás, Abel, and Penelope, who was now fourteen. But more than anyone else, she ruled Dad. In her eyes, Dad was the chronic loser who couldn't support his family. Mom had to implore her cousin, who was big in the landscaping business, to give Sal Ruiz a job. Now Sal worked every day at backbreaking tasks, doing grunt work. To Abel, he was a poor mule with a swayback who endured a life of grinding toil with no hope for anything better.

"Sal," Mom commented, turning to her husband. "Tomás was never moody. He was always such a cheerful boy. He was always such a joy to be around. Wasn't he a joy to be around?"

"A joy," Dad agreed. He agreed with everything his wife said.

"Even when Tomás had problems, he would discuss them with us," Mom recalled fondly.

"Abel, what is wrong?" Liza Ruiz demanded, lasering in on her son again. "Stop that texting! Are you insane? That's all you ever do around here. I would like to smash that cell phone. You text every minute of the day. It's like we didn't exist, your father and me."

The woman's face then hardened, and a knowing gleam crept into her eyes. "It's that girl, isn't it? It's that Claudia Villa. I never liked that girl, not from the first moment you took up with her. Stuck-up snotty girl from that private school. Cesar Chavez High School wasn't good enough for her, don't you know. She's what's making you depressed, isn't she? It has to be her. My mother always said a woman can make or break a man. I believe that. Isn't that true, Sal?"

"Yes, very true," Dad replied, looking as though he wanted to say more. But he just looked sad. Abel could tell what he was thinking, though. The poor man would never put his bitter thoughts into words.

"It's got nothing to do with Claudia," Abel lied.

Penelope, who was a freshman at Chavez, came into the room and looked at her brother. Abel and his sister had never gotten along well, but they usually tolerated one another. In Abel's mind, Penelope was always sort of obnoxious, though he did admire the fact that she occasionally rebelled against Mom. Though Penelope was nicely built, she was a little plump. So whenever she ate a chocolate bar or a cookie, Mom looked stricken. Sometimes Penelope stuffed her face with sweets, just to stick

4

it to her mother. That amused Abel. Now, however, Penelope said the wrong thing.

"I bet Claudia Villa has ditched you for somebody else, Abel," she declared. "And that's why you're moping around."

"Mind your own business, *gorda*!" Abel retaliated.

"I'm not fat," Penelope screamed, hurling a magazine at Abel. It almost knocked the cell phone out of his hand.

"Stop it!" Mom shrieked. "I will not have my children fighting!"

"I'm not a child," Abel fumed. "I'm almost a man. After I finish high school, I'm gonna move as far from here as I can." Abel stalked off to his room and loudly slammed the door behind him.

Alone in his room, Abel plopped down on his bed. He was fuming. What made him so mad was that his mother and his nosy little sister had gotten it right. It *was* about Claudia. A few weeks ago, everything was fine in Abel's life, at least as fine as it could ever be for him. He wasn't a genius, but he

5

was making decent grades in his classes. He was even making a solid C in his worst class, English lit. He stood a chance of getting an A in math. He was sure he'd nailed an A in science.

Then, a little over a week ago, Abel asked Claudia to the movies that Friday night. She had really wanted to see the movie, one of those chick flicks she loved. Abel endured them just to please her. Claudia gave Abel some lame excuse about why she couldn't go. She mumbled something about a sick aunt. Abel was suspicious right away. He and Claudia had been close for quite a while now, and he could read her pretty well. When she was lying, she got a funny look in her eyes. He didn't think she had a sick aunt.

Abel really loved Claudia. She was his first real girlfriend, and she made a huge difference in his life. Just about every morning when he woke up, thinking about her gave him joy. He couldn't bear the thought that she might be going from his life.

So on Friday night, Abel did something that he hated himself for. What he did was low and sneaky, but he couldn't stop himself. Abel drove over to Claudia's house and parked on the next street. He left the car and hid behind a row of heavy shrubs across the street from Claudia's house. Then he watched. He had a gut-wrenching fear that some dude would pull up in a nice car, and he and Claudia would go off together.

It happened at seven. A gray Ford Ranger pulled into Claudia's driveway. She came running out. She looked fabulous in distressed jeans. She was wearing that lime green pullover she looked so good in. Abel had told her several times how hot the sweater made her look.

Claudia got into the truck, and away they went.

Abel's heart sank when he got a look at the guy. He had chiseled features and long curly hair. He looked like a hunk. Abel figured he was a student at that private boys

7

school. Social events at both schools were held together. Claudia probably met him at a dance run by both schools.

Abel had hurried back to his car, hurt and confused. He was ashamed of spying on Claudia, but his gut feeling had been right. She was cheating on him. No, he told himself sternly. You couldn't call it cheating. They were in high school. They didn't have a commitment. Still, Abel thought Claudia was *his* girl.

At the doughnut shop the next Monday, Claudia was as nice and friendly with Abel as she always was. They worked together dishing out chocolate, powdered, and multicolored sprinkle doughnuts. Claudia acted as if nothing was wrong, but, for Abel, *everything* was wrong.

"Are you okay, Abel?" Claudia asked him at quitting time.

"Yeah," Abel replied, avoiding looking her in the eye.

"You don't act like yourself," Claudia commented. "You're not sick or anything, are you?"

Abel was confused all over again. She was acting as if they were still close, as if she *cared* about him. Maybe the dude in the Ranger was a cousin, he thought. Maybe he was getting all upset over nothing.

Or was she worried that Abel might be on to her? Did she think he'd found out about her and she didn't know how to handle it? Was that what brought worry into her eyes?

"I'm okay," Abel mumbled. "Lotta homework and stuff."

Abel's boss at Elena's Donut Shop was Elena's brother, Hector Ponce. He was a lot easier to work for than Elena had been. He was an easygoing guy, and he gave nice raises to good employees. And normally both Claudia and Abel were dependable workers.

But during the past week, Abel had been short with a few customers. Worrying about Claudia had messed up Abel's usual friendly style. Hector had called him on it. "Hey, Abel," he said, "there's a lady, a regular customer, she complained about you. She said you were impatient and rude when she took a while to decide on her doughnuts. Hey, buddy, we have to be nice to the paying customers."

"Yeah, sure, Hector. I'm sorry," Abel replied.

On Tuesday night, Claudia and Abel were on duty at the doughnut shop again. Leaving for work, Abel grabbed his jacket and headed for his VW Jetta. Maybe tonight Claudia would explain the guy in the Ford Ranger, he thought. Maybe she'd lift the dark cloud hanging over Abel's head.

"Abel," his mother called after him. "Be careful driving. It's drizzling."

"Yeah, Mom," Abel snapped.

"Listen to me, Abel," Mom persisted. "The police say the roads get very slick when it first rains after a dry spell. You can hydroplane or something."

"Yeah, yeah," Abel grumbled.

"Abel," Mom said, coming to the window of the VW. "You're acting too strange. You're not on something, are you? You're not doing drugs, are you? *Santo Dios*, it would kill me if you did such a thing!"

"I'm not on drugs, Mom," Abel insisted. "I gotta go."

He connected his seat belt and backed out of the driveway. In his mother's eyes, Abel was the weak one in the family. Tomás, the brilliant engineering student, would never have been questioned about being on drugs. Tomás, the saint, would never think of doing such a thing. But if Abel was acting a little strangely, Mom easily believed he was stoned on something.

Abel drove to work through the darkness. He was shocked at how the fear of losing Claudia was derailing him. Once they had gotten close, Abel just assumed it would go on like that. Claudia would stick with him. She always seemed so happy and

11

content on their dates. She seemed to have as much fun as Abel did.

Claudia was with a customer when Abel came in. He slipped on his white shirt and joined her at the counter.

"Hi, Abel," Claudia greeted, smiling at him. She didn't seem the same, though. Her warm brown eyes were clouded. Something seemed to be on her mind that she couldn't easily talk about. Had she found a new guy? Was she struggling with how to tell Abel? Abel's mind spun in agonized circles.

Maybe, thought Abel, her parents were on her. They were always nice to Abel. But he kind of knew that they would have preferred Claudia to have a boyfriend from the private boys school. Maybe they were putting pressure on Claudia to date other boys, boys who were more her own kind. Claudia was good, dutiful. She wouldn't stand up to her parents and demand the right to choose her own friends.

As the evening went on, Abel noticed Claudia glancing nervously at him. She looked unhappy.

As quitting time neared, Claudia came over to Abel. Then she spoke the words Abel dreaded: "Do you have a few minutes after work? There's something . . . I need to say."

"Sure," Abel said, feeling numb.

"Daddy isn't picking me up until nine-thirty," Claudia added.

"Okay," Abel said. His mouth was so dry that he was surprised he could get any words out at all.

After work, Claudia and Abel sat in his Jetta. She looked down at her hands a few times, and then she spoke. "I'm sorry I lied to you, Abel. I never meant to do that. It was awful. I'm so ashamed. I really wanted to go to the movies with you Friday. But Daddy had a good friend from high school coming over, and the guy had a son. Daddy wanted me to go out with his friend's son.

His name is Victor Toro, and he's a student at the boys high school, the private one."

"You shoulda just told me that, Claudia," Abel told her. "I'm not the kind of guy who thinks he owns a girl or something. Just 'cause we've been hanging out doesn't mean you can't do stuff like that. You know, if your dad asked you."

"I know, but I felt weird," Claudia explained. "I thought it was kinda disloyal to be out with another guy. Especially after I lied about the sick aunt. I don't even *have* an aunt around here."

"You were just doing a favor for your dad," Abel assured her. "He wanted you to show his friend's son a good time. The dude is probably shy or something. His father wants him to go out with a hot girl like you to sorta break the ice. Is this Victor shy?"

"No, not really," Claudia admitted, looking at her hands again. She twisted a silver bracelet on her wrist nervously. Abel figured she wasn't telling him the whole truth yet. Finally she spoke again. "Mom and Dad sorta don't like the idea of us—me and you—dating. Like, you know, always being together. Mom and Dad, they're going . . . like you're too young and stuff. Dad told me I'm too young to be going out with one guy . . . this is the time I need to be with a lot of people. You know . . ."

Abel was feeling better about his chances. In his mind, Claudia was explaining her actions but still wanted to be his girl. "Claudia," he told her, "you know that I respect you. I wouldn't push you into anything you didn't want to do. If your folks have a problem with me, then maybe I need to talk to them."

"No, no, they like you fine, Abel," Claudia protested. "It's not that at all. It's just that they want me to experience as much as I can while I'm still young. They don't want to see me, you know, get tied to one relationship."

Claudia swallowed. "My parents are very strict. They're scared if I'm getting

15

too close to one boy. Then there might be problems."

"Claudia, there would never be problems with me. You know that," Abel assured her.

"Sure, Abel, I know," Claudia agreed, "But my parents are very old-fashioned, and they read these magazine stories about stuff happening." Claudia's eyes widened then, and she got out of the car. "There's Daddy now. I better go."

Mr. Villa got out of his van and walked toward the Jetta. Abel and Claudia both got out of the car.

"Hi, Abel," Mr. Villa greeted. "How's it going?"

"Okay," Abel responded. His heart was pounding. He didn't think he had the whole truth yet, maybe not any part of the truth.

"Did Claudia tell you she would like to spread her wings a little bit?" Mr. Villa asked in a friendly but very businesslike voice. "I mean, listen, you're both kids, right? You and Claudia both should be dating other people. Kids your age need to play the field. You know, find out what life is really like before you settle down."

Mr. Villa smiled broadly and winked. "Otherwise, how in the world are you ever going to know what you really want in life? When I was in high school, I dated half a dozen girls, and I'm glad I did. It helped me to know the kind of girl I wanted to settle down with. Why, you're not even through high school, and then there's college. Good grief, you're very young!"

Abel looked at Claudia. Her father was telling him a very different story. Claudia made it sound as if she went on a date with some guy to please her father's friend. But now Mr. Villa seemed to be saying that he and his wife had a big discussion with Claudia. He seemed to saying that Abel wasn't going to be part of Claudia's life anymore. Claudia stood nearby, looking embarrassed and nervous.

"If Claudia doesn't want to see me anymore, that's okay," Abel replied. His

17

heart was pounding crazily. He felt numb and lightheaded, but he tried to keep it all together. He felt like something inside him was ripping apart, but he kept cool. He didn't want to lose it.

"Abel, no!" Claudia stammered.

"You kids just need a little time out . . . a little space," Matt Villa asserted in a firm voice. He sounded friendly, but he wasn't smiling. "You've been a little too intense, don't you think? Mrs. Villa and I talked about it. We both thought you were too close for kids your age. Things were going a little too fast."

Abel didn't say anything. Glancing toward Claudia, he noticed tears running down her face. She turned sharply and ran to her father's van, sliding back the door and getting into the backseat. Abel wanted to run over to her in the van. He wanted her to know that he still cared about her. He wanted to say that, if this was her decision, then he respected it. But if her parents were forcing this on her, he wanted to tell her to be

18

strong. Both he and Claudia would be eighteen soon, and they had the right to make their own decisions. Abel wanted to talk to her and tell her she was free to do what she wanted to do, no matter what that was.

But Mr. Villa turned abruptly, walked to the van, and got behind the wheel.

Abel didn't know what to think. He wanted to believe that none of this was Claudia's idea. He wanted to believe that with all his heart, but he wasn't sure.

Abel watched the van drive off. He leaned against his VW Jetta, his eyes closed. He felt as if he'd been hit in the stomach with a baseball bat.

Abel's mind kept going in two directions. One minute he thought Claudia still wanted to be with him, but her parents were forcing a separation. The next minute he thought Claudia was losing interest in the relationship herself. He figured she was using her parents' objections to make it easier for herself. He didn't know what to believe.

One thing for sure, Abel thought. Naomi Martinez would not do this to her boyfriend, Ernesto Sandoval, no matter what her parents said. Ernesto Sandoval was not popular with Naomi's father for a long time. But Naomi stood with Ernesto.

And Carmen Ibarra would not do this to Paul Morales, no matter what her parents said. Abel remembered when Carmen's parents were very upset about her dating Paul Morales. It was a struggle to get them to allow Paul in the house.

So why was Claudia doing this to him? Why couldn't she stand up to her father? Why couldn't she say she wanted to keep dating Abel Ruiz?

But Claudia just cried and hid in the backseat of her father's van. Abel didn't know what that meant. Was she just weak? Or was Abel Ruiz not worth fighting for? Was he, like his mother always said, a loser after all?

CHAPTER TWO

Abel couldn't talk with anyone in his family about what had happened with Claudia. He wasn't close to his father, and, anyway, Dad shared everything with Mom. Abel could just hear his mother's high-pitched wail. "Oh, poor Abel! I knew that girl was no good for you. Didn't I tell you she wasn't for you? The stuck-up little snob, thinks she's better than everyone else because she goes to that private school. I saw that right away. Poor Abel. You must feel terrible! This is so humiliating!"

The only person Abel could talk to was his best friend, Ernesto Sandoval. Abel didn't want to tell the gang, the kids he hung with every day at lunch. He just wanted to go off somewhere and talk privately with Ernie. Whatever he told Ernesto would go no further. Ernesto wouldn't be gossiping about what happened between Abel and Claudia. Abel punched in Ernesto's cell number.

"Yeah?" Ernesto answered.

"Ernie, it's Abel. Listen, any chance I could pick you up at your house now. Maybe we could hang out at Hortencia's for half an hour? I know it's late but . . . ," Abel asked.

Ernesto didn't hesitate. "I'll be out front waiting, dude. I was just watching some lame stuff on YouTube."

"Thanks," Abel said with relief.

Ernesto was waiting in front of his house on Wren Street. When Abel came by, he jumped into the Jetta, and they headed for Hortencia's. Hortencia Sandoval, Ernesto's aunt, owned Hortencia's restaurant and tamale shop. The place had nice secluded booths for talking. Hortencia was Ernesto's father's youngest sister. In her early thirties, she was young and pretty. She planned to marry Oscar Perez, who had a lively Latin band in Los Angeles. Hortencia was popular with everybody, especially the young people.

"Hey, man, thanks a lot for this," Abel said.

"Anytime, homie. What's going down?" Ernesto asked.

"Claudia, she dumped me, man," Abel confessed. "I knew she was acting weird lately, but I didn't see this coming. Tonight, after work, her father cornered me. He put on this big rant about me and Claudia being too young to be so close. She needed to see other guys. Oh man, it went on and on. It blew me away, man."

"I'm sorry, dude, really sorry," Ernesto said.

"Yeah," Abel murmured. "You know, I been worried about how she's been acting. The other night she turned down going with me to a movie she really wanted to see. Told me some bull about a sick aunt. Anyway, I

23

drove over there and saw her jump into a Ford Ranger with another guy."

"She's already got a new boyfriend?" Ernesto asked in surprise. "That doesn't sound like Claudia."

"Nah, she said this dude, Victor Toro, he was the son of her father's old friend," Abel responded. "She sorta let on that she had to go out with the guy to please her father. But I wasn't buying that. I think she's into this Toro guy. He goes to the boys school nearby her private girls school. He looked like an A-list jerk. Football-player build. Looked way better than me, man. I think Claudia is starting to see who I really am, a wimpy little nobody. She's looking for something better." Abel's low self-esteem was crushing him.

"Knock it off, Abel," Ernesto insisted. "You're a good-looking, smart guy. You're a genius in the kitchen with a bright future. I don't know what's going on with Claudia. Did you ask her how she really felt about you guys?"

Abel just shrugged. They were pulling into the parking lot at Hortencia's. They didn't speak as they went inside and found the most remote booth in the back. Once seated and waiting for their orders, Abel spoke.

"I was going to ask her straight if she didn't want to see me anymore," he said. The waitress put their hot chocolates down.

"And she said?" Ernesto demanded.

"I never got a chance to ask," Abel answered. "Just then her father came along, and he did all the talking. He told me he thought we were too young to be together all the time. I still don't know if he was just helping her dump me."

Abel sipped his hot chocolate with a hurt look on his face. Then spoke again. "I looked over at her while her dad was going on. She was crying. I guess that's something."

"Abel," Ernesto declared, "you need to know what's going on here. I've always liked Claudia, and I figured you guys were good for each other. But Claudia is a kinda sheltered girl, so maybe this is all about her parents. I mean, her parents probably control her a lot more than most parents of the kids at Chavez, you know? So you gotta find out where she's really coming from, man."

"Ernie," Abel responded, "you remember when you first started going with Naomi? Old Felix Martinez didn't treat you right. He would have preferred that thug, Clay Aguirre, for Naomi. He said you were a weakling or something. Same with Carmen. Her dad didn't want her dating a dude with a rattlesnake tattooed on his hand. To them, he was just a guy who hangs with wannabe gangbangers. But Naomi and Carmen, they stood up for themselves. How come Claudia doesn't, you know, stand up for herself—*for us*?"

"Dude, like I been saying, the girls at Chavez are more independent. They're tougher," Ernesto said.

"Ernie, I really care about this girl. You hear what I'm saying?" Abel said, his voice breaking. "I can't keep on working at that doughnut place with her. I can't keep seeing her all the time, knowing she doesn't like me anymore. I mean, it'd be like rubbing salt in a raw wound, man."

"I understand, Abel," Ernesto responded. "But before you do anything, talk to her. Ask her how she really feels. Last time you wanted to ask her, her father was right there. He did all the talking. When you get the chance at work, ask her. Okay?"

"Yeah, yeah, you're right, man," Abel agreed, nodding yes. "I was gonna call Hector Ponce tomorrow and tell him I wasn't coming in anymore. I mean, my head is spinning. But that'd be wrong. I feel like somebody cut my legs out from under me, Ernie. I really needed to talk to you. Thanks for being here."

"Abel, I got your back," Ernesto assured him. "Don't you ever forget that. You're the best friend I ever had. I'm not ever gonna forget that, man. When I first got to Chavez, I felt like I just stepped off a spaceship. I

27

didn't think I'd make it, but you got me through. You were my rock, *amigo*."

Abel smiled a little. "I feel a little better. I'm not so crazy in my head, you know. Maybe Claudia's parents have her backed up against the wall. Maybe the worst thing I could do is desert her now. Maybe she needs me now more than ever."

"Right!" Ernesto agreed. "Just go back to work, be nice and friendly like. When you get the chance, ask her how she honestly feels. Don't diss her parents or anything. Just say you know she's a chick who really obeys her parents. Let her know you know what she's up against."

"Ernie, I owe you one," Abel said. "One of these Sundays I'll be over to your house to make you guys *gazpacho*. I've learned to make it over at the Sting Ray. That dude, Pedro, he's amazing. I'm learning so much from him. This *gazpacho* has roasted shrimp and *piquillo* peppers and an *epazote* leaf. It's got all the things you can only get in Mexican grocery stores. You'll love it."

Ernesto grinned. "You don't owe me, but I'll take it."

The boys finished their hot chocolates, talking about other things. Abel dropped Ernesto home before going home himself.

Abel drove to his house on Sparrow Street. He was still worried about Claudia. But talking to Ernesto had lifted his spirits and given him hope.

"Abel," Mom called to him as he came in. "Why are you so late? I expected you home an hour and a half ago. I was worried sick that you'd had an accident or something. I called and called your cell phone, but you had it turned off! It kept transferring me to voice mail. I was ready to call the police!"

"Everything's okay, Mom," Abel insisted. "I forgot to turn on the cell phone." Abel was usually irritated by his mother's overprotectiveness. Usually, he would have said something. But Ernesto made him feel better, and he didn't want to argue with anybody.

29

The next day, Abel was walking toward the Cesar Chavez school library. He was still feeling pretty good until he heard a familiar, unpleasant voice. Clay Aguirre's voice was harsh and mocking. "Hey, I guess you know what it feels like now, huh, dude? Your chick stuck it to you just like mine did."

Abel tried to ignore Clay. Naomi Martinez had dated Clay for a long time before she started going with Ernesto. But Clay was a creep. He treated Naomi like dirt and finally he hit her, badly bruising her face. Naomi dumped Clay after that. Now Clay was taking out his anger on Abel. He kept up his taunting.

Finally, Abel snapped back at Clay. "I don't know what you're talking about." Abel continued walking toward the library, but Clay followed him.

"I saw Claudia at that chick flick Friday night," Clay went on, gleefully. "She was with a real hunk. They were like hot and heavy, man."

Clay had caught up to Abel, and now he was walking beside him. "You're such a good *amigo* of that jerk Sandoval. Now you know how I felt when he snatched away my chick. I loved Naomi. Still do sometimes. It grinds me every time I see her with Sandoval. She and I were cruising, man. Then he came along and broke us up."

Abel finally turned and looked Clay right in the eye. "Dude, you're not fooling anybody. You didn't deserve the girl. You punched a girl in the face and left her bruised. That was low, man. You're nothing but a bully and a creep. Ernie didn't take her from you. She dumped you because you're trash."

"Yeah? So me and Naomi had a little fight," Clay snarled. "Yeah, okay. I shouldn't have hit her, and I was sorry. I apologized a dozen times. It never woulda happened again. Naomi woulda forgiven me. We woulda gotten back together—better than ever—if Sandoval hadn't made a move on her. So, Ruiz, how's it feel when you're the one gettin' dumped?"

Abel wanted to punch Clay right in his leering face, but he didn't dare. Chavez had a zero tolerance rule for fighting on campus. "Aguirre," Abel growled, "why don't you find a sewer pipe and crawl down there with the other rats?" Then he spun on his heel and stomped off to the library.

When Abel got to the library, he checked out the old seafood cookbook he'd been hunting for. Then Clay's words hit him. Claudia had gone to the chick flick that she and Abel were going to see together. She and Victor Toro saw it. She let Toro take her to *their* movie.

Claudia had talked so much about that movie. She told him all about the characters she liked and disliked. Abel tried to appear interested just for her sake, although he really didn't care. He was just happy listening to her.

Abel tormented himself by going over the past few weeks. He made himself crazy

32

looking for small clues that maybe Claudia was getting tired of him. Had he missed the clues? He felt as though he wasn't the sharpest guy in the world. Maybe Claudia was feeling bored, and he didn't even notice. He was just so happy to be with her that he probably wouldn't have noticed little signs. But all he remembered were her laughter and her sparkling brown eyes. If she was upset or tired of him, she hadn't shown it.

Yet Abel remembered one time when he thought Claudia wasn't having fun. It was the first time Abel felt something might be wrong. It was just before the beach party. Claudia had always loved evenings at the beach. This time, she didn't seem enthusiastic about going. Abel had picked her up at her house, and her parents were as cordial as usual. The couple shopped for the stuff they were bringing to the party, but Claudia seemed preoccupied.

When Abel made some of his lame jokes, Claudia always giggled. But that night she didn't. Abel asked her if she was all right, and she said she was. But she just wasn't herself as they drove to the beach.

Abel remembered her standing on the sand, forlornly looking out over the water. He came up beside her and put his arms around her shoulders, as he often did. She pulled away and said she had to check on something. Abel felt hurt. She'd never withdrawn from his touch.

Abel had wondered then whether he'd said something without thinking. Maybe he had hurt Claudia's feelings. Sometimes Abel said stupid things that he didn't mean, just to get a laugh. Claudia never seemed to mind. She always played along. Maybe she resented some comment he'd made about her. He vaguely remembered telling her that she sort of looked like some girl singer on YouTube. But that girl was a little overweight. Maybe that hurt Claudia's feelings. Claudia was very trim, and maybe she resented being compared to a girl with a lot of curves.

But Claudia wasn't usually sensitive. She wasn't easily hurt. Abel remembered other times when he said stupid things, and Claudia just laughed. That was one of the many things he loved about her. You never walked on eggs with Claudia.

Why all of a sudden would Claudia become thin-skinned?

When Abel got home from school that day, he heard his mother yelling at Penelope. Mom was angry—ticked. Abel often thought Penelope was a pain in the neck, but he put up with her.

He noticed, however, that Penelope had turned more rebellious. That happened after she finished middle school and became a freshman at Chavez. She wasn't a bad-looking girl, and she never paid much attention to clothes styles. But since she'd started at Chavez, she jumped on the new clothing fads, and some of them made her look awful. She went overboard with the layered look, and Abel thought she looked ridiculous. Sometimes, as Penelope left for school, she looked as though she was wearing everything in her closet.

But right now Mom was steamed about something more serious.

"All my friends have boyfriends!" Penelope shrieked in an unusually shrill voice that hurt Abel's ears. He figured the pitch was higher than a police siren. "I feel like some kind of a freak, Mom."

"Penelope," Liza Ruiz answered in a voice almost as shrill. "You're a child! You're only fourteen years old! I didn't even think of dating until I was past sixteen. Even then, my parents didn't let me go out except in a group. I was seventeen years old before I went on a date alone with a boy."

"That was a hundred years ago," Penelope screamed. "They didn't even have TV or telephones or maybe even cars then."

"Penelope Ruiz," Mom yelled, "that was only twenty-five years ago. Oh, we certainly did have television and telephones and cars. What we didn't have is rude children who were disrespectful to their parents!"

Abel tried to sneak unnoticed to his room. He had enough on his plate worrying about his future with Claudia. He didn't need to get mixed up in his little sister's love life. But Mom spied Abel before he could make good his escape. "Abel!" she cried. "Can't you talk some sense into your sister? You're a boy. You know what happens to little girls when they get involved with boys at too early an age."

"Abel is an idiot!" Penelope screamed. "He doesn't know anything about anything."

"Penelope! Don't talk that way about your brother. Shame on you," Liza Ruiz commanded. "Abel, tell this child what you were like when you were fourteen?" Mom was pleading.

Abel glared at his sister. He was still stinging from being called an idiot. "No guy is gonna want you anyway, Penelope," he

37

told her. He was being deliberately mean to her. "You're a giant, and all the boys in the freshman class are midgets. You've seen them. They don't want to mess with chicks who're a foot taller than them. Most of the little freshman guys don't want any chicks, period. They sure don't want to mess with a big clod like you."

"That is so stupid," Penelope retorted. "I'm not that much taller than mosta the other girls. I just had my growth spurt a little earlier than the other girls. Look at that really hot actor who's in big movies all the time. He's much shorter than his wife. Anyway, a couple ninth-grade boys are already smiling at me."

"They're probably laughing at you, girl," Abel crowed. "You're not only a giant, but you wear so many clothes that you look weird. No normal chick wears six blouses and ten sweaters all at the same time. You look like you stole it all, like you're sneaking out of the mall with it on."

"Liar!" Penelope screeched. "I don't do that. I look nice when I go to school. All my girlfriends say I look really cool."

"They're afraid of you," Abel snickered. "You're so big, they don't tell you the truth. Besides, I don't think you *have* any friends."

"Stop it, you two!" Mom demanded. "Why can't you be nice and helpful to each other like Tomás was when he was at home? Do you remember, Abel, when you were younger? Tomás was always showing you the ropes. You boys had such a loving, friendly relationship."

Abel stared at his mother without answering. He wanted to tell her she needed a reality check, but he didn't. Abel remembered the merciless ribbing he got from Tomás when he was Penelope's age. The guy never missed an opportunity to get Abel. Mom insisted it was all in good-natured fun, but Tomás was always the only one laughing.

In fact, Tomás's teasing often got cruel. Abel couldn't count the times he found his

39

shoes tied together. Tomás used to get up early so that he could tie the shoelaces of Abel's shoes together. The knots were so ingenious that Abel couldn't untie them.

Abel didn't want to get into his bad memories of Tomás. And he wanted no part of fighting with Penelope either. He just stated what he thought. "Penelope's a jerk. She won't get a boyfriend anyway, Mom, so why are you getting so crazy over it? Nobody at Chavez is dumb enough to want to be seen with her."

"You're just being nasty, Abel, 'cause your girlfriend dumped you," Penelope finally screeched. She fell silent, looking as though she had scored a big triumph. She was grinning from ear to ear, reminding Abel of a very evil-looking jack-o'-lantern. "It's all over Chavez that Claudia has another boyfriend," she added, this time not screaming. "That's why you're being so mean!"

"You don't know what you're talking about," Abel snapped. In his heart, though, he knew that the gossip about Claudia and him was spreading at school. That was all thanks to Clay Aguirre and his friends.

"It's true," Penelope chirped. "Roxie Torres has a sister in my freshman English. She said, 'I hear your brother got dumped by that snooty girl.'"

Abel waved a dismissive hand at his sister and hurried down the hall to his room. He slammed the door behind him and sat down with his laptop. He had to do some research for science. He sat there staring at the screen for a while, unable to focus. Then he closed his eyes, and his fingers tightened into fists, which he drummed on his knees.

Abel felt sick and scared. He felt as though everybody in the world knew what had happened to him while he still clung to foolish hope.

CHAPTER THREE

It took Abel several days to work up enough courage to do what Ernesto suggested— ask Claudia where they really stood. Abel was terrified that the answer would destroy him. He tried to push off the pain. Then, on Tuesday evening, when business was really slow and Abel was making coffee, he glanced over at Claudia. She was filling the jelly doughnut tray. Abel stared at her lovely profile for a few agonizing seconds. He felt shaky. Abel wasn't sure he could handle the truth. But Ernesto was right: Not knowing was the worst torment of all.

"Claudia," Abel began in a voice that cracked a little. "Something's going on between you and me. I'd like to know where we're at. You don't have to cover anything up, Claudia. Just tell me the truth about how you feel about me, about *us*. I need the truth."

Claudia stopped filling the tray with jelly doughnuts. She chewed on her lip.

"If your parents don't want me around anymore, Claudia, just tell me," Abel continued. "I'm not gonna be mad. I'm not going to put pressure on you."

"It's not my parents," Claudia finally confessed. She looked at Abel. This was so hard for her. She looked indescribably sad. "Abel, you're the nicest guy I ever knew. I care about you. I care about what happens to you. I mean, we've had so much fun together. I'll never forget that. I didn't want anything to happen that would change things."

"'Didn't'?" The word exploded in Abel's brain.

Claudia looked away. She put another couple of doughnuts on the tray. After a second or two, she went on. "But . . . it was

43

my cousin's eighteenth birthday party, and there was this guy there. Victor Toro. He goes to the boys school that's paired up with my school for social things. I'd never seen him before. Victor and I started talking. We talked and talked, and we danced." Claudia began to cry.

"You liked him, huh?" Abel asked softly.

"I just felt so excited, so happy," Claudia explained. She sniffed and reached for a napkin from the dispenser. She dabbed at her eyes. "It was like those stupid things that you think only happens in the movies. You see somebody, and your whole world changes. I told my parents. They tried to help me out with that stuff Daddy was talking about, about us being too young and all that. It was just a cover story, Abel. My parents like you. Mom used to even joke about when you and I are maybe married. You know, I'll be lucky 'cause you'll do all the cooking."

Claudia looked down at the tray of doughnuts. "But Victor just made me feel so incredible."

44

Abel's mouth was bone dry. He doubted he had enough saliva in his mouth to swallow. He felt numb. For some crazy reason, he did not expect this answer. He had been clinging to the belief that Claudia felt the same about him. He'd suspected that her parents were pressuring her to break off the relationship. Until this moment, Abel thought maybe he could fix things by talking to her parents. He could convince them that he was a good guy, worthy of their daughter.

But this was different. This was a deal breaker, and it hit Abel like a tsunami. He recalled the news footage of that huge wave sweeping everything away in Asia. He felt as though he'd lost everything worthwhile.

"Okay," was all he could whisper weakly.

"Oh, Abel," Claudia sniffled. "The last thing in the world I ever wanted to do was to hurt you." Her eyes teared up again.

"Yeah, well, stuff happens," Abel responded through the dust in his throat.

He went back to making the coffee. Every few seconds, he checked the clock. He willed the minutes to go faster so that he could get out of there. After what had just happened, he didn't think he could stand another second so close to Claudia.

Luckily, a family with three noisy children came in. They took a long time to choose a dozen doughnuts. The oldest girl was about eight, but she reminded Abel of Penelope. She had a grating, strident voice. She demanded doughnuts that nobody else in the family liked. The family was a welcome distraction that lasted until it was time for Abel to go home.

"Abel," Claudia said as he grabbed his coat and headed for the door. She wanted to make a better apology. She wanted to tell Abel what a nice guy he was. She wanted him to know how sorry she was that she had fallen for another dude. But Abel didn't want to hear any of that. All of it just came down to a heartbreaking truth: Claudia

Villa didn't want to be with Abel anymore, and Abel wanted to die.

"Night," Abel replied, without turning and looking at the girl. He rushed through the door and jumped into the VW. He started the engine with one hand and put his seat belt on with the other. The car spun out of the lot, the tires throwing gravel.

Abel didn't drive directly home. Instead, he drove to the bluff overlooking the beach. He got out of the car and sat on the rocks, watching the dark water splashing below on the sand. Moonlight was silvering the waves. It was a beautiful night. A few weeks ago, he and Claudia were down here. They had just sat in the car and snuggled in each other's arms. Abel was on top of the world that night. How quickly it had all vanished for him just didn't seem possible.

Abel knew one thing: He couldn't go back to the shop and work side by side with Claudia as if nothing had happened. He couldn't face seeing her night after night.

He had to quit that job and maybe get more hours at the Sting Ray to make up for the lost salary. He didn't have any doubt that Pedro would gladly add hours. Pedro liked Abel and his work a lot.

But Hector Ponce had been good to Abel. It seemed wrong just to suddenly quit and leave Hector in the lurch. The doughnut shop was the support of Hector's big family. If he lost a key employee without the chance to break in somebody new, his business would be affected.

Abel wrestled with his dilemma for a while. Then he grabbed his cell phone and called Paul Morales. Paul, Claudia, and Abel had worked together at the doughnut shop before Paul quit. Abel thought Paul might know an experienced guy who could quickly step in for Abel.

"Hey, Paul," Abel said when Paul answered the ring, "I got a big problem."

"Yo, Abel, shoot," Paul responded.

"Paul, I'm in a bind, man," Abel explained. "I need to quit the doughnut shop

48

like right now. It's like a personal problem. I was wondering if you knew any dude who could come on right away and do my job. I'd hate to leave Hector in the lurch. I don't want Hector stuck with a bunch of customers and somebody who doesn't know what they're doin'. He's always been straight with me, and I don't want to screw the man."

"Where are you now, man?" Paul asked.

"I'm parked at Crescent Overlook at the beach where we had the barbecue," Abel answered.

"I got Cruz's van—my wheels are in the shop. See you in ten minutes," Paul said.

"You don't have to do that, Paul," Abel protested. "I just need to get in touch with somebody who could take my place."

"See you in ten minutes, dude," Paul insisted.

In less than ten minutes, Paul parked the wildly decorated van behind Abel's Jetta and parked. He walked over and sat down beside Abel. "Claudia, eh?" he said.

"How'd you know?" Abel stammered.

"It ain't no secret, homie," Paul replied.

Abel dropped his head and closed his eyes. Clay Aguirre and his friends were spreading the story all over Cesar Chavez High. Even Penelope knew it. Of course, Paul heard it, probably from Ernesto. Paul was aware of almost everything that went on in the *barrio*.

"Dude, listen up," Paul commanded in a harsh voice. "You're gonna be a man about this. Otherwise, you'll suffer for it in your heart and your brain for a long time. You're gonna go back to the doughnut shop. You're gonna give Hector your two weeks' notice like a man would, like the man you are. You're gonna be—"

"Paul, I can't," Abel groaned.

"Yeah, you can," Paul insisted. "You'd be surprised what you can do. You're more man than you ever dreamed you were, dude. You're gonna go back there and be polite and cool. You're not gonna let that chick see you bleed, man. It won't be easy. But you can do it, Abel. You're

50

a class act, homie. I always admired you for that."

Abel still had his head down. He was not responding.

"Look," Paul went on, "Let's say it's ten years from now. Claudia's sitting across the kitchen table from some creep who isn't a quarter of the man you are. And she's gonna be remembering the dude she dumped because her little hormones got to firing up. She's gonna turn on the TV and see a hot young chef on the food network. She's gonna have a lotta regrets about what might have been."

Paul grasped Abel's shoulder and squeezed it a couple of time as he spoke. "You think about that while you're putting in your two weeks, Abel. That's what'll get you through. Revenge is the best painkiller there is at a time like this, homie."

"Paul, I don't hate Claudia. I mean . . ." Abel started to say.

"Look, dude, she didn't play fair," Paul objected. "If she found someone else, she shoulda been up front from the beginning. She shouldna played this little cat-and-mouse game. You guys were tight. You shouldna been left hanging in the wind, homie, while almost everybody else in the *barrio* was on to it. So when you feel like a knife is turning in your heart, you think about ten years from now. You'll probably have the hottest chick in the Southwest, and she'll appreciate you for who you are, dude. Tonight, it's Claudia's loss, man, not yours."

Paul slapped his friend on the back and stood up. Abel got up too. They stood there watching the waves overrunning the sand.

"I'm not sure I can pull it off, man," Abel remarked.

"You *can*, Abel," Paul insisted. "I swear to you, you can. I've known a lotta dudes—the good, the bad, the half and half. They don't come any better than you. After you've done your two weeks, you'll feel like an even bigger man than you are now. You're a magician with food, Abel. That Pedro at the Sting Ray, he'll snatch you up like a kid grabs an ice cream cone in July. You're too good to be doing doughnuts anyway."

Paul swung around to face Abel. He bent down to look up at Abel's face. Then he flashed that big Morales smile and grabbed Abel in a bear hug. "You're healing already, man. I can see it in your eyes. You're gonna make it just fine."

When Paul drove off in the van, Abel decided he would do what Paul suggested. Abel's first impulse had been wrong. He'd let his emotions overrule his good sense. If he ran from the doughnut shop like a wounded rabbit, everybody would have the laugh on him. Paul was right. Abel figured that right now he didn't have much going for him. But he had his pride, and that was a lot.

Abel spent another half hour or so at the beach that night, hatching his plan. The rest of the week, Abel didn't share a shift with Claudia. So he waited until Saturday night to ask Pedro, the Sting Ray owner, whether he could get more hours.

"I love working here," Abel explained, "and I'd like to quit the doughnut shop. Then I could spend the freed-up time working here where I'm learning so much."

A wide grin split Pedro's dark face, revealing the big gold tooth in front. "*Muchacho*, you got a deal," he responded in his thick Mexican accent. "I'll give you all the hours you want. You're the best, man. Business is up since you're here. The young people especially. They like to see a young chef coming up. You're friendly, smart, and cool. You add the right touches, stuff I don't even think of. The other day we offered the olive oil poached halibut, remember, *amigo*? You came up with the idea of garnishing it with seaweed. Everybody raved about it."

Pedro shook his head and smiled broadly, as if to say, "No problem, my friend." He gently rapped his knuckles on Abel's chest. "You just let me know when you want more time."

"Okay, thanks!" Abel exclaimed, touched by the man's enthusiasm. "I gotta give two weeks' notice at the doughnut shop, and then I'm all yours."

"I respect you, Abel, that you're giving a decent shake to the doughnut guy you work for. That shows character," Pedro remarked, slapping Abel on the back.

On Sunday afternoon, Abel told his parents about the change. "I won't be working at the doughnut shop anymore," he stated in a matter-of-fact voice. "I'll be working more hours at the Sting Ray instead. I'll be earning more money an hour. Plus, I'll be getting really good experience in what I want to do with my life. So it's win-win."

"They fired you, didn't they?" Mom gasped. "Oh, Abel, that is so terrible. After all the time you worked there!"

Abel gave his mother a long, hard look. "They didn't fire me at the doughnut shop, Mom. I'm giving them my two weeks' notice and quitting, okay?"

"It's 'cause he doesn't want to work with his ex-girlfriend," Penelope remarked. "Claudia dumped him for some jerk at that uppity private school."

Abel decided not to take his sister on. He had enough to deal with. "The thing is, I'm gonna be learning a lot at the Sting Ray. I'm tired of dishing out doughnuts."

At the doughnut shop on Monday afternoon, Abel went to Hector Ponce immediately. The guy had always been fair with him, and he liked Hector. "Mr. Ponce, I'm giving you my two weeks' notice. I've really enjoyed working for you. You're a cool guy, and you've always treated me right. I'll miss working for you, Mr. Ponce. But I got this chance to work more hours at this upscale restaurant. And that's the kind of experience I need to get."

"Abel, I hate to lose you," Mr. Ponce responded sincerely, "but I've been expecting this. I hear these stories about you catering big meals for your friends and really showing your stuff. I've seen this coming. Guys like you, they're rare. You're not the run-of-the-mill kid working at a food joint. You got to look out for your own future. I hate losing you, but thanks for the two weeks' notice. You got class, kid. I'll never find another Abel Ruiz, but I wish you all the luck in the world."

Abel shook hands with his boss and went to work. The hard part was still ahead. Claudia was coming on duty in about five minutes. He'd have to face her. He'd have to work side by side with her, seeing her cute profile, smelling her special fragrance.

Abel tried to remember Paul's advice: "You're gonna go back there and be polite and cool. You're not gonna let that chick see you bleed, man."

When Claudia came in, Abel forced himself to look at her, smile, and say hi. Then he turned his attention to the dough-nut trays he was filling.

Claudia looked nervous. "Hi, Abel," she replied. Abel thought it had to be hard for her too. She was probably as uncomfortable as he was right now. They were both busy for about ten minutes. Two families and a guy buying doughnuts for his office gang had come in. Then there was a lull.

"Oh, Claudia, just to let you know," Abel said in a calm voice, though inside he was shaking. "I'm going to be working more at the Sting Ray starting in two weeks. Pedro offered me a lot more hours. So I've given my two weeks' notice here. It'll be good for me."

"Oh," Claudia responded. "Well, congratulations. I mean, it's a step up for you."

Abel thought to himself, "Don't let her say she'll miss me. Please don't let her say that. It would be such hypocrisy."

"It'll seem strange you not working here," Claudia commented. "You're fun to work with. It's been a long time we've been dishing out doughnuts together."

Abel said nothing. He filled a tray with freshly baked crullers. They were very popular.

58

To Abel's surprise, Paul Morales, Cruz Lopez, and Beto Ortiz came in a little later. They hadn't been in this place for ages that Abel remembered. Paul had had a big fight with Hector Ponce's sister, Elena, way back when she ran the shop. At the time, she had accused all the employees in the shop of stealing from her. It turned out her own teenaged daughter was the thief, but not before she targeted Paul as the likely culprit. Now Abel had the sneaking suspicion that Paul and his homies had come in to lend Abel moral support. The three boys lined up at the counter and ordered coffee and Danish pastries.

"So, Abel, you're gonna be working at the Sting Ray, huh?" Paul asked in a friendly, boisterous voice. "That's great. Much better than dishing doughnuts, homie," He glanced at Claudia. When Paul worked at the shop, he and Claudia got along fine, but they were never close. "Hey, Claudia, how's it going?" he inquired.

"Okay," Claudia said in an awkward voice.

"Yeah," Abel replied, "working at the Sting Ray is gonna be good for my future. I learn a lot there."

"That place is too rich for my blood," Cruz remarked, whistling. "Man, they charge an arm and a leg for four jumbo shrimp. But someday I'll scratch up enough money to treat Pop and my sisters to a dinner there."

"Hey, dude," Paul said, looking at Abel. "You planning to catch the car show next Sunday?"

"I don't know," Abel answered.

"You gotta come. It's gonna be the best car show ever," Paul urged. "They're showing some awesome new wheels, man, like the latest BMWs."

"Them babies get about three hundred thirty horsepower, dude," Cruz said. "They'll go from zero to sixty in six seconds. Man, what I'd give to drive a machine like that."

"And they got the new Escalade," Beto added. "Awesome."

"You know what I'm going for, though?" Paul asked, a big grin breaking out on his face. "I'm not going 'cause I think I can afford any of those fancy cars. They're gonna have the hottest chicks in the universe sitting atop the hoods. And they'll be wearing no more than they have to. They get models and babes from all over, and they make a guy's eyes pop right out of his head. You know, Abel, that's why you gotta go. That auto show has more eye candy than you ever saw in your life."

"Yeah," Cruz said, "chicks in flame red bikinis. I went last year. These chicks were wrapping themselves around my neck. It was like I was the hottest dude that ever lived. Me! Made me feel good, I'm telling you. Good for the soul, man."

Abel knew what was going on. All this was for Claudia's benefit. The message was that Abel was doing just fine without her and that it was only going to get better.

The three boys—Paul, Cruz, and Beto—broke into fits of gleeful laughter. They poked each other in the ribs and left out no details.

Claudia looked very uncomfortable. She almost knocked over a tray of chocolate doughnuts.

"I guess I better go then," Abel agreed. "I wouldn't want to miss the car show. Sounds like fun."

"I know one of the chicks who're gonna be working the show Sunday," Paul said. "I'll introduce you to her, Abel. She's got legs that reach all the way to the ground. Y'hear what I'm saying, homie?" Paul laughed and said, "This chick is so hot you gotta be wearing sunglasses just to look at her."

Abel's friends were really laying it on thick, but their antics touched Abel. He knew they were his friends, especially Paul. But he never figured they cared so much about his pain. Here they were, coming around like this and putting on a show just for him.

CHAPTER THREE

Abel knew beforehand that tonight would be the worst. He'd figured if he could get through this shift, then the rest of the days and evenings wouldn't be too bad. He could hold it together if he made it through tonight. He could cover his pain, and Claudia wouldn't see him bleed. That was what it was all about.

And that was why Paul and his homies were here, to make it a little easier. And it was working, at least a little. By the time Paul and the others left, Abel felt stronger. Paul Morales was right. You had to tough it out. Abel's heart was still breaking every time he glanced at Claudia, but now he thought he could come away a man.

CHAPTER FOUR

Every morning, when he woke up, the first thought in Abel Ruiz's mind was about Claudia. They had been together almost six months, and she'd become a precious part of his life. He usually sent her a text message as soon as he woke up in the morning. In two minutes he'd get one back. No big deal, just connecting. And her cheery little good morning text would put a smile on Abel's face. The day would get brighter. The tough test coming up in math didn't look so ominous. Mom's nagging was bearable. Penelope's annoying ways became trivial.

It was hard getting used to the fact that Claudia was gone. In painful little steps, Abel was getting used to living without her.

At the breakfast table this morning, Penelope poured too much milk on her corn flakes, as usual. Then she complained loudly that they were too soggy. She couldn't eat them because they were "gross." That was the morning routine. Mom nagged. Penelope whined. Dad sat in safe, stoic silence. Abel could tell when his father's bad back was troubling him again. Abel watched his dad's sad eyes narrow, and he winced when he moved.

Mom brought Penelope more corn-flakes and poured the milk herself. After that, for some reason, Penelope seemed almost pleasant. "I told my friend, Dani, that you were gonna be all the time at the Sting Ray," she said to Abel. "And she goes, 'Oh, that's such a ritzy place. My uncle eats there all the time, and he's rich.' And like she couldn't believe a guy who's still in high school would be cooking there."

"It's a very nice place," Abel commented.

"Dani's mom said you must be pretty good to work there as a cook," his little sister remarked. "I mean, you're not a bus-boy or something."

Abel couldn't imagine why his sister was being nice to him. For a fleeting moment, he thought he must look so sad and depressed. Maybe she thought he was dying or something, and this was her last chance to be kind to him. Or maybe Penelope wanted some huge favor.

But Penelope finished her breakfast and didn't ask Abel for a favor. She spent extra time picking out her best jeans and a new top for her ride to Cesar Chavez High. Then she wheeled her bike from the driveway.

"I could drive you," Abel offered. "I'm going there too, you know."

"I'd rather ride my bike," Penelope replied. "I'm riding with a friend. We both ride our bikes together, and it's fun." She turned to Abel then and asked, "Can you keep a secret?"

"I guess so," Abel replied, standing in the driveway looking at his little sister straddling her bike. Usually Penelope annoyed Abel. But looking at her now, he thought she was pretty cute in her skinny jeans and sky blue top. She wasn't a bad-looking fourteen-year-old.

"There's a boy who likes me," Penelope confided, her cheeks flushing. "Don't tell Mom. Promise?"

"I won't," Abel promised. "He a freshman at Chavez too?"

"Yeah," Penelope answered, as she pedaled away.

Abel left for school only minutes later. Since he was going to work from school, he took the Jetta and didn't jog. He thought he might pass Penelope biking along with her friend, but he didn't. Penelope had the bad habit of texting when she rode her bike. Abel was going to call her on that if he saw her doing it. Texting was distracting to a biker too.

At the school lot, Abel parked the Jetta and began walking toward his first class. Penelope was talking with a group of her friends. He wondered how she got to school so fast. He was driving, and she beat him on her bike.

"Hey, Penny!" Abel called to her. "How'd you get here so quick? You beat me in the car." Penny just shrugged her shoulders and laughed. Then she continued chatting with her friends. She seemed to really be in a good mood.

As Abel continued walking toward his first class, he ran into Julio Avila, who was heading for the same first class as Abel.

"Hey, dude," Julio said, "I think I saw your brother this morning."

"Tomás?" Abel asked in surprise. "He's up at college. He's not coming down to visit for a coupla weeks that I know of."

Julio shrugged. "I don't know your brother, man. But just I saw this good-looking dude about twenty driving your sister to school. I figured it had to be your older brother."

"This morning?" Abel gasped. "A guy brought Penelope to school?"

"Yeah," Julio replied. "He was driving a tricked-out ride. You always said your older brother was a hotshot, so I just thought it was him. But I guess not, huh?"

"Tomás doesn't drive anything tricked out," Abel responded. "You saw Penelope in the car with this guy?"

"Yeah, man," Julio said. "She stashed her bike in the back of the car. When the dude pulled up to the school, she dragged her bike out again and put it in the bike rack. Something going on, Abel?"

"I don't know," Abel said. "Penelope is a pain in the neck most of the time. But she's my kid sister, and I gotta get to the bottom of this."

It wasn't time for class yet. So Abel walked over to where Penelope and her friends were still talking.

"Penny," Abel asked. "See you for a minute?"

Penelope looked annoyed, but she broke away from her friends and came over. "What's the matter?" she demanded.

"Some guys saw you getting dropped off here at school by a dude, girl." Abel got right to the point. "You had your bike in the back. What's with that?"

Penelope's face flushed, and her eyes widened. "That's a lie. Whoever told you that is a big liar. I rode my bike to school. It's right over there in the bike rack, for crying out loud. Your weirdo friends are telling you lies, Abel."

"I was wondering how you coulda beat me to school," Abel commented. "I was driving, and you were on a bike. I left home right after you, and when I got here you were already yakking away with your friends. Penny, give it to me straight. What's going on?"

"I ride fast," Penelope insisted in a shrill voice. "Don't you make trouble for me, you big dummy! I rode my bike to school like always. I don't know what your crazy friends are talking about. They must have mistaken another girl for me. Some stupid jerks are telling you lies about me, and you believe them. You're so dumb! No wonder Claudia dumped you! You're just a big fool!"

Abel ignored her fury. It just proved to him that she *was* hiding something. "You're always posting stuff on Facebook, and you're talking to people you don't even know. Did you connect with some creep, Penny? Is that what happened?" he demanded.

"Abel, I swear if you say anything about this to Mom, I'll never forgive you," Penelope threatened. "I'll hate you forever and ever. I didn't do anything. I just rode my bike to school like I always do. I rode really fast 'cause my friend who usually rides alongside me didn't come today. That helped me get to school faster. That's all it was. If you tell these lies to Mom, she'll ground me and take my iPhone and my laptop. I'll be ruined. I might as well be dead! You can't do this to me, Abel. You just can't!" The girl seemed on the verge of hysteria.

"Okay, okay," Abel said calmly. "But don't be doing anything stupid. Don't *ever* accept a ride with a stranger. You're a kid.

Any adult guy who'd pick up a kid is a dangerous creep!"

Abel wasn't satisfied with how the conversation ended. But his sister was making a big scene, and he had to get to class. He met up again with Julio, and they walked into the classroom together. They had a few minutes before the teacher came in, so Abel turned to Julio. "Dude, are you *absolutely* sure you saw Penelope riding with some guy? You saw her get out of his car and take her bike? Are you like totally sure?"

"Yeah!" Julio asserted. "I don't do drugs and hallucinate man. I didn't think anything of it 'cause I thought it was her brother. The guy looked about twenty, twenty-one."

"She denied it, the little sneak," Abel said bitterly. "I bet she's got something going with some freak she met online. They're out there like vultures looking for girls. This is bad, man. She's just fourteen years old. Most of the time I'd like to push a pie in the little twit's face, but she's still my sister. I gotta look out for her. What kind of a slime ball would want to hang out with a fourteen-year-old when he's like past twenty? It makes my skin crawl, dude."

"Yeah," Julio agreed, "you better tell your parents to lower the hammer."

"Mom'd freak," Abel objected. "She'd ground Penny till she's eighteen! I'm telling you, man, it'd be a disaster. Mom's craziness would drive Penny to run away."

"How about telling your dad?" Julio suggested. "Maybe he could handle it better. After all, a father knows how to protect his daughter, right?"

"My father's a wimp, Julio," Abel confided. "He'd go to Mom right away. Maybe a long time ago, Dad had a backbone, but it's gone now. Mom's got him trained like a seal. She says 'Jump,' and he'll go, 'How high?'" Abel groaned.

Abel kept his eye on Penelope after school. He watched her head for the bike rack and start the ride home. Abel looked around the parking lot and the street for the guy's car, but he didn't see it. There was no sign of the dude, but that didn't console Abel much. If some older guy out there had something going with Penelope, she was in danger, maybe big danger.

Abel went to his VW and dialed Paul Morales. He told him briefly what was happening. "I'm worried sick, dude," Abel admitted. "I gotta go to the doughnut shop now, but I had to tell somebody. I don't trust Penelope. She's so nuts for a boyfriend. I think she'd climb in the car with King Kong if he was wearing pants."

"Okay, homie," Paul told him. "I'll meet you in the parking lot of the doughnut joint. I still got Cruz's van."

Just as Abel was pulling into the doughnut shop's lot, Paul pulled in alongside him. He stopped nose to tail, so the two drivers could talk without getting out.

"Hey, man, this doesn't sound too good," Paul commented. "She go home with the creep after school?"

"No, I watched her until she got on her bike," Abel answered. "I drove down

74

Sparrow before I came here, and she was at our house."

Cruz and Beto were in the van with Paul. Cruz said, "We'll shake the trees, man. We'll ask around who knows a dude who drives that car. Don't see too many of those in the 'hood."

"Yeah," Paul added. "We'll get the dope on the freak. I gotta go to work right now. But I'll get back to you as soon as we learn anything, dude. We got to nip the thing in the bud. No man worth spit should be hanging' with a little fourteen-year-old chick."

"We got lots of homies who know just about everything that goes down around here, Abel," Beto noted. "We should get something pretty quick."

"Then we'll deal with the dude," Paul declared with an ominous glint in his eyes.

"Thanks, you guys," Abel said. "Penelope, she's my *hermana*. I don't like her, but I love her, you know?"

Paul and Abel fist-bumped, car to car. Abel waved good-bye to the others as he got out of the car and started toward the store.

When Abel got into the doughnut shop, Claudia was texting somebody. She was smiling as she used to smile at Abel. She giggled a little. It was like a knife in Abel's heart. Abel had seen the look in her eyes before, but this time it wasn't for him. He stiffened and focused on his work. The doughnut trays needed filling. The napkin holders were empty. Two lights needed replacing.

As he worked, Abel thought that Claudia had been his greatest treasure. He would have done anything in the world for her. Why didn't their relationship mature into something permanent? He would have broken his back to provide for her, to make her happy. Nobody in the world would ever love her more.

Abel felt a burst of deep bitterness. *Why were chicks so stupid*? Couldn't they tell when a guy loved them so much and would never let them down? Why did they let a rush of hormones ruin everything?

Even Ernesto Sandoval's girlfriend, Naomi Martinez, had put up with that ugly Clay Aguirre for so long. He insulted her in public, shoved her around. Ernesto had to work so hard to rescue her from that rotten relationship. Why did chicks go for the creeps and get bored with nice guys who loved them so deeply?

And Penelope, the little *boba*, she was the same. No doubt she met some flashy creep online. Then she was stupid enough to jump in his car and ride to school with him. He was probably twenty—nineteen at the youngest. He was probably a bad boy. Bad boys were more exciting, Abel thought.

Abel was never a bad boy. He was a good guy who was respectful to girls. He would never have insulted or hurt one of them. What kind of guy was this Victor Toro that Claudia flipped over? Yeah, he went to a private school and all that. His parents had a lot more money than Abel's parents did. But did he treasure

77

Claudia as much as Abel did? Or was he some shallow jerk with good abs and a nice set of pearly whites? Would he enjoy Claudia's company for a while and then move on?

"Hi, Abel," Claudia said when she was done texting. "How's everything?"

"Great," Abel responded, remembering Paul's advice. Don't let her see you bleed. "I'm excited about being at the Sting Ray more hours."

"I'm glad for you, Abel," Claudia told him. She sounded sincere. Maybe she was. She was a nice girl, not a mean person. She couldn't help it that she was weak and that some dude came along and swept her off her feet. "Of course, that guy probably made me seem lame by comparison," Abel thought.

Abel grimly put in his shift. He served the customers with a smile and did all the things that endeared him to the customers. He joked with the little kids, promoting the new apple fritters. And then it was time to go off duty, and he rushed for the door. It was dark, and the crescent moon high in the sky near Venus shed no light.

The first thing Abel saw was the decorated van parked next to his Jetta. Cruz jumped out first.

"Climb in the van with us, man," Cruz directed. "We got work to do."

"We'll bring you back here to get your car when we're done, homie," Paul said when Abel was in the van.

As the van pulled out into the darkness, Abel asked, "You find the guy who took Penelope to school?"

"Yeah," Paul said with disgust. "His name is Max Costa." Paul spat out the words like bullets. "Nineteen years old."

"Whoa!" Abel cried. "Julio said the guy looked lots older than the kids at Chavez."

"Yeah," Paul responded. "He works as a night watchman at the recycling place on Jefferson. He goes off duty at ten thirty. His car's parked on the street. One of Cruz's friends remembered seeing that car there."

Abel didn't question what they were about to do. He was leaving things in Paul's hands. He knew that was maybe risky, but he couldn't handle it himself. He was shocked that a nineteen-year-old guy would have anything to do with a kid like Penelope, a fourteen-year-old freshman. Something had to be done. Abel was going to let things play out the way Paul thought was best.

They parked the van on a side street, and the four boys walked toward Costa's car. It was a rough part of town, and the walls of the buildings were heavily marked with graffiti. It was dark too. The city didn't spend a lot of money on replacing shot-out street lights around here.

Costa's car sat in a pool of darkness. The boys stood back in the shadows, watching.

A little after ten thirty, a well-built young man in a leather jacket appeared. He was coming from the recycling plant toward the car.

"That's the dude," Paul hissed.

Max Costa was almost in his car when they jumped him. Paul and Cruz overpowered him and slammed him to the ground, face down. Beto yanked his hands behind his back.

"No!" Max Costa whined. "You guys, take what you want, but don't hurt me. Please. You can have my iPhone . . . my wallet. Just don't hurt me."

They dragged him to his feet and pinned him against the chain-link fence that surrounded the recycling center. Beto snapped several pictures of Max Costa on his iPhone. He snapped front view and profile.

"What's going on? What is this?" Costa gasped.

Three of the four boys—Paul, Cruz, and Beto—wore hoodies, and they looked like gangbangers.

"Listen up, man," Paul snarled harshly. "You're some excuse of a man, you know? You're nineteen years old, and you been hitting on a kid, a little girl from Chavez High School."

"No, I haven't," Costa stammered. "You got the wrong guy." He was ashen and shaking.

"You picked up a fourteen-year-old girl and drove her to school, dude," Paul told him. "Penelope is fourteen years old. You understand that, pond scum?"

"No, no, she said she was seventeen, a senior at Chavez," Costa answered. "I swear, she said she was seventeen."

Paul grabbed Costa's shirt front and shook him as a cat shakes a rat. "She's a little kid. A *niña*. Anybody can see that. So listen up, dude. We got your picture, and we got your license number. If ever a little girl is missing within five hundred miles of here, we go to the cops, get it? They're gonna be on you like flies on road kill."

Abel finally found his voice. "Penelope's my little sister," he piped up. "Don't you ever go near her again. Don't go online and try to talk to her. Don't text her. Don't go within a mile of Cesar Chavez High School."

"I swear I won't," the young man gasped. "I swear I won't. I'm telling you, I didn't know she was fourteen!"

Beto whipped out a switchblade and flipped it open within an inch of Costa's face. Abel knew that Paul and his friends carried them, but he'd never seen one actually in their hands. A chill ran up Abel's spine. What was Beto about to do?

Beto tapped the tip of the blade on Costa's throat. "Stay away from kids, man. Stay away from kids, or you're gonna be face down in some alley. Then you won't be waking up on this earth, man."

"I swear I won't go near that school or the kids," Costa cried.

Beto closed his switchblade, and Paul shoved Costa back against the fence. The four boys turned and walked toward the van. They climbed in, and the van vanished in the darkness, leaving Max Costa leaning against the fence, still shaking. Out of fright, he vomited, and then staggered to his car. After a few minutes, he drove off.

"Man, I never been in the middle of something like that before," Abel declared. He was sweating profusely.

Paul Morales laughed. "We scared that little creep so bad he's gonna be wanting to date *viejas* after this."

"I owe you guys," Abel declared. "I was worried sick about Penelope."

"Listen up, Abel," Paul said. "You talk seriously to your sister. I wouldn't be surprised if she did tell that snake she was seventeen. She's a pretty tall kid. He knew she wasn't, of course. But she's playing with fire."

Paul shook his head in disgust and went on. "All the little chicks around here, they're going online. They post their pictures and put themselves out there. They're like little small-fries swimming past great white sharks. Abel, you watch what she does online. You tell your mom to monitor her. You don't have to rat Penelope out. Just tell your mom what's happening with kids."

"Yeah," Beto agreed, "a little fourteen-year-old on her way to high school, she was picked up and murdered by some bad dude a few years ago."

"To think that Penelope would get in this guy's car when she didn't even know him," Abel gasped with a shudder.

"Drive her to school," Paul insisted. "Tell your mom that bad dudes are hanging in the 'hood; Penelope needs to be driven to school for a while. Your mom'll go along with that."

"Penelope will hate me," Abel responded, "but I don't care. I'd rather have her hate me and be safe than have her love me and be attending her funeral."

"Right," Cruz affirmed. "I got a little *hermana* coming up, almost Penelope's age. I'm gonna be watching her back too, man. That's the way it's gotta be. The cops aren't able to protect the kids. There are too many bad guys and not enough cops. It's up to us, the *familia*."

Abel didn't think he'd ever seen anyone as frightened as Costa was. "Hey, guys," he asked, "did anybody see what happened when Beto tickled Costa's throat with the switchblade?"

No one replied. "Well," Abel went on, "you guys were busy. You couldn't have seen. The creep wet his pants."

The van exploded in laughter.

They dropped Abel off in the parking lot of the doughnut shop, and Abel gave each of his three friends a heartfelt hug. Then Abel got into his Jetta for the drive home. He almost missed the Ford Ranger over in a dark corner of the parking lot. A guy and a girl were locked in each other's arms.

The girl was Claudia.

Abel felt like a fool as his vision blurred with tears. At least Claudia couldn't see him as he drove from the parking lot and headed for Sparrow Street.

CHAPTER FIVE

In the morning, Mom was making breakfast before anyone else was up. Abel went to the kitchen and spoke in a low voice. "Mom, I think I should drive Penny to school in the morning. I'll drop her back home before I go to work."

Mom was making scrambled eggs and ham burritos. She stopped to stare at Abel. "Is something wrong?" she asked.

"Well, some of the kids at school said guys have been hanging around, you know," Abel lied. "These guys seem to be watching the girls who walk or bike to school. They're older guys, maybe eighteen or nineteen. It's probably nothing, but I think it'd be safer if I drove Penny for a while."

"Oh *Santo Dios!*" Mom cried in her high-pitched voice. "If somebody kidnapped my Penelope, I would perish in grief! Yes, yes, Abel, it's a wonderful idea. Bless you for thinking of your sister like that. I know she's not always nice to you, but you are a good brother anyway. Oh, Abel!" Mom abandoned her burritos and came over to embrace Abel, something that surprised him. "*Mi hijo!*" she cried emotionally.

"Yeah, yeah," Abel mumbled, extricating himself from his mother's arms. "You can tell Penelope this morning, Mom, but don't tell her I talked to you about it. Tell her your friends, some of the other mothers, told you. Okay?"

"Of course, yes, yes," Mom agreed.

When Penelope appeared at the breakfast table, she was frantically texting. She seemed frustrated as she sat down to eat her cornflakes. She was not getting a text back. Abel didn't know for sure, but he suspected who it was that she was trying to text. After last night, Max Costa no doubt never wanted to hear the name "Penelope" again in his natural life.

"Honey," Mom directed, "put the phone away. I don't want you texting at the table."

"I can't get a friend," Penelope objected. "I'm worried."

"Never mind," Mom said. "Just put the phone away. Eat your breakfast."

"Oh!" Penelope growled. She stuffed her cell phone into her jacket.

"By the way, Penny," Mom announced, "some of my friends called me. They said there are unsavory characters hanging around Cesar Chavez High. They're going to be driving their daughters to and from school just to be on the safe side. I think it'd be better if you went to school and came home with Abel."

"Nooo!" Penelope screeched. "I love riding my bike to school, and it's good exercise. I meet all my friends, and it's fun. It's the best part of the whole crummy day!"

Abel focused intently on his burrito. He added more salsa. He didn't even look at Penelope for fear she would detect the guilt in his face.

"Penelope," Mom commanded firmly, "Abel is going to drive you this morning, and he's going to bring you home. That's it. I'd never forgive myself if I'd heard this warning and ignored it. What if something dreadful happened to you? My friends are worried and so am I. A few years ago some poor little fourteen-year-old not far from here was picked up and murdered on her way to school. It was only about six miles from here."

"Mommy!" Penelope wailed. "It's not fair!"

Abel's father rarely got involved in the child rearing problems of his family. He usually just sat silently and let his wife take care of things. But now he looked up from his coffee and spoke calmly. "Penelope, you have to listen to your mother. She loves you, and she wants to protect you."

"But it's not fair," Penelope continued howling. "It's like I'm being grounded, and I didn't do anything to deserve it."

Abel thought to himself, "Yeah, *right*."

Penelope glared at her cornflakes. "I'm not going to eat this garbage now. It's all soggy and yucky," she declared.

"You want a burrito?" Abel asked. "They're really good."

"I don't want a stinking burrito," Penelope snarled. She got up from her chair and grated it across the floor, making a tooth-chilling noise. "I might as well be in reform school! I might as well have a warden!" she wailed as she walked to her room, madly texting again.

Abel sneered to himself. Max Costa would not answer. Not after he met Paul, Cruz, and Beto last night.

When Penelope climbed into the passenger side of the Jetta, she glared at Abel.

"You didn't have anything to do with this, did you?" she demanded to know.

"Me?" Abel replied innocently. "I got my own problems." He backed out of the driveway.

As they drove to Cesar Chavez High, Penelope's head was swiveling around constantly. Abel knew she was looking for Costa's car. She thought he'd be here today, looking for the cute little girl on the bike. Penelope began texting again.

When Abel parked, he turned to his sister. "After the last bell today, come here and wait for me. I don't hang around talking, so you won't have to wait long."

"This is so unfair," Penelope griped. She was texting as she got out of the car.

"Penny, doesn't your thumb ever get sore?" Abel asked. "I text too, but not every minute."

"Oh shut up!" Penelope snapped, jumping from the car and running to join her friends. Abel figured that Max Costa would just mysteriously disappear from

Penelope's life, and she'd never know why. Abel wasn't sure what the guy was really like, but he had to be a creep to make a move on a kid. Maybe he believed she was sixteen or something—or wanted to believe it. Even then, he was a grown man. He was an adult. He had no business with a kid. He probably went after Penelope because he knew he could manipulate her. Maybe he wasn't dangerous, but he sure wasn't any good for Penelope. And maybe he *was* dangerous.

Abel was proud of what he and his friends did. Maybe it was a little over the top, but they'd spared Penelope trouble. And maybe they'd scared the creep off connecting with underage girls for good.

Abel went to his English class. Grace Lauer was the teacher, and she was an ardent fan of nineteenth-century female writers. Ms. Lauer was a tall, angular woman with pretty, dark eyes and a quick smile. She especially liked Emily Dickinson.

"You have all read and analyzed the two short poems we introduced last time,"

Ms. Lauer began. "And now I'd like to know which one you found superior, and please give me lucid reasons. Choose either "Death Is a Dialogue" or "If I Can Stop One Heart from Breaking." And keep in mind what we talked about. There are good poems, and there are great poems. Ms. Dickinson never wrote bad poetry, but some of her work was outstanding."

Carmen Ibarra's hand shot up, and the teacher acknowledged her. "I liked 'If I Can Stop One Heart from Breaking,'" Carmen announced. "Because it really said something important. I like for poems to mean something. That's why I don't like a lot of poems that they're writing now. Because they don't make sense. But I know you won't agree with me, Ms. Lauer, because obviously the other poem is superior because it's more obscure."

Ms. Lauer laughed. "You obviously have a good grasp of poetry, Carmen."

Abel didn't like poetry at all. Even concentrating in this class was hard for him. Instead, he was thinking about once when he and Claudia were taking a walk. They came across a strange flower, the night blooming cereus. It is a magnificent, big white flower that blooms just one night and gives off a glorious perfume. Then it dies. That night, Abel and Claudia were at the beginning of their relationship. That night, he believed they were going to be together for a long time, but they were doomed like the white flower.

"Abel," Ms. Lauer said. "Abel?" She had to call him twice to rouse him from his daydreaming. "What do you get out of 'Death Is a Dialogue'?"

"I don't know," Abel answered. He hadn't even read the poem.

Clay Aguirre snickered. Naomi Martinez raised her hand and answered for Abel. "It's a commentary on everlasting life. Death says to dissolve, but the spirit will go on. It sheds what Ms. Dickinson called the 'overcoat of clay,' which is a metaphor for our body."

Abel thought to himself that he would like to dissolve right now. He wanted to forget about Claudia Villa. He wanted to erase her lovely oval face from his memory so that she would stop haunting him.

After school, Penelope was standing by the VW, waiting for Abel. She didn't look angry anymore, just sad. She wasn't texting either. She had given up.

When Penelope got into the car, she asked, "You know what, Abel? I told you about this boy who sorta liked me . . ." Her voice was soft and vulnerable, not belligerent as it often was.

"Yeah," Abel responded.

"Well, he dumped me," she said glumly. "He just totally dumped me. I thought he liked me. I know that's stupid 'cause he was a little older. I mean, I was so excited. So many of the freshman girls are really hot, and the boys are drooling over them. He was the first boy who seemed to like me."

"That's, uh, tough," Abel replied. "You said the guy went to school at Chavez. What's he got to say?"

"Well, I sorta didn't tell the whole truth, Abel," Penelope confessed. "I mean, he's not a freshman at Chavez like I said. I sorta met him online, and we both liked the same music. I tried texting him today, but he's just not there."

"Maybe he's not the guy you thought he was," Abel suggested.

"He said he had a little band," the little sister said. "They played indie rock. That's so cool. He's uh . . . a little older than me. He's sixteen."

"Where does he go to school?" Abel asked, knowing Max Costa was long gone from the classroom. It sounded like maybe both Penelope and Max lied to each other.

"He said he was a junior at Lincoln," Penelope answered convincingly. She said nothing for a few seconds. Then she said, "I guess I told him I was a junior at Chavez. I mean, I didn't want him to think I was some stupid baby."

"Well, things don't always work out, Penny," Abel said, glancing over at his sister. "Listen, I don't have to be at the doughnut shop for an hour. Want to get a mocha or a frappé at the coffee shop?"

Penelope brightened. "Yeah!" They hadn't gone anywhere together in a while. Abel and Penelope had gotten along well when he was about ten and she was seven. As they got older, they got on each other's nerves.

When they were in the coffee shop waiting for the frappés, Penelope spoke. "You probably feel lots worse about Claudia than I do about Max. That's his name. Max. I didn't get his last name. I mean, I thought he'd tell me when we got together again."

"Well," Abel thought, "at least we scared the beans outta the right guy."

Out loud, he said, "You know, Penny, you oughta hang out with guys your own age. It's kinda dangerous making friends online. You never know where they're coming from. This Max guy could be even older than sixteen, you know? Maybe you saw him on Facebook, but he really is just a baby-faced adult,"

"The freshman boys are all jerks," Penelope grumbled. "They make stupid, gross jokes about the bathroom and stuff. And they're short and creepy looking. Max was so . . . cute."

Abel smiled a little. "The boys at school will get better, Penny. But, yeah, I feel lots worse about losing Claudia than you feel. We been together for a long time."

"What happened? You guys have a fight or something?" Penelope asked. "And she got the new boyfriend to stick it to you?"

"Nope," Abel admitted. "Claudia just met another guy she liked better than me."

"I guess stuff like that happens to people even when they're married sometimes," Penelope mused. "A lotta my friends got stepmoms and stepdads. The kids are one weekend living with their real dad and the other weekend with their mom and some guy. It gives me the creeps to think something like that could happen with our parents. You don't think it ever would, do you?"

"No," Abel answered firmly.

"Good," the girl responded, "I'd hate for Dad to move away with some other lady and for Mom to bring some creep into our house. It would be so revolting." Penelope finished her frappé. "You'll probably find another girlfriend, Abel."

"No," Abel objected. "I don't want another girlfriend. It hurts too much when it goes sour."

"Never?" Penelope asked, her eyes wide. "You *never* want another girlfriend?"

"Maybe when I'm old, like twenty-five. Maybe then," Abel replied.

"Maybe she'll come back," Penelope suggested. "Maybe Claudia'll get sick of the new guy and come back."

"Wouldn't be good anymore," Abel said, finishing his frappé. "Wouldn't ever be the same . . ."

"Yeah," Penelope agreed as they walked out together. After she got into the car, she said, "This was nice. Thanks."

"You're welcome," Abel replied, in a moment of rare friendliness.

Abel felt a little funny about deceiving his sister. He didn't like pretending he knew nothing about what happened with the guy she liked. But if he'd told her the truth, she probably would have ended up hating him. And, even if Costa was on the square, there was no future in the relationship with his little sister anyway. They started out lying to each other. There was no way in the world it would have been right for a fourteen-year-old kid to be hanging with a nineteen-year-old man.

Abel glanced over at his sister in the passenger seat. He didn't know how much of a creep Max was, but he had no business connecting with kids online. Penelope didn't even look fourteen. She was tall but looked thirteen. She still had that round little girl face. It couldn't have gone anywhere but to a very bad place. So Abel had no regrets. If he had it to do over again, he would do the same thing.

Later in the day, when Abel arrived at Elena's Donut Shop, he was surprised to find Elena Suarez there. In the beginning, Paul Morales, Claudia, and Abel worked for her. It was a nightmare. She kept missing money from the till and blaming her employees, especially Paul Morales.

Elena Suarez had a drinking problem and lots of boyfriends. Her daughter, Sarah, was out of control. She hung out on the streets all hours of the night, trying to date older boys. Sarah was only thirteen when she ran away to be with her father in Mexico. The last Abel heard, Sarah was living down there.

"Hello, Abel," Elena greeted him. "How is everything?"

"Okay," Abel lied. "I'm a senior at Chavez now. After I graduate, I'm going to culinary school. I wanna be a chef."

"Wonderful!" the woman replied. "I have good news too. I'm getting married next month. I tried to work it out with my ex-husband in Mexico, but it just didn't fly. I met a marvelous man at the casino, and we hit it off right away." Elena Suarez was a plump, pretty woman who looked even younger than she was.

"Great!" Abel said weakly. "Sarah doing okay?" Abel remembered the little girl with sadness. She wasn't a bad kid. She was just desperately lonely and caught up in a bad family situation. Her mother had no time for her, and her father took her in reluctantly.

For just a moment, the woman's eyes clouded, and she looked sad. She quickly composed herself and managed a forlorn smile. "Sarah passed away last summer," she sighed.

Abel was stunned. A thirteen-year-old doesn't just pass away. Sarah was vibrant and full of life. Sarah's uncle, Hector Ponce, had never said a word about his niece's death. Not a word to any of his employees. Abel's head swiveled from Elena to Hector once or twice. Hector said nothing.

"I'm really sorry to hear that," Abel told her. "I didn't know. I would have, you know, sent flowers or something." Abel and his friends had gotten Sarah off the street and home late one night. Her mother was too drunk to even know the child was on the streets getting into trouble.

"I know, Abel," Elena responded. "Thank you for the kind thoughts. She was sick. We didn't know it at the time, but the child had mental problems. She just couldn't fit in. I tried . . . her father tried. I was so busy with the doughnut shop that I didn't see what was happening. I was just trying my best to keep everything together. I missed the signs."

Abel wanted to ask how Sarah died. He remembered the vividly pretty girl, looking like a younger version of her mother.

He remembered the girl's need for parents, who were never there. Sarah even tried to date Abel when she was thirteen, and he was seventeen. He was horrified. He couldn't believe it. But Sarah had insisted she *always* hung out with older guys. Abel told her she was a child and he was a man, but she didn't seem to care. She just wanted to have somebody to love her.

"She ran away, over and over again," Elena Suarez explained, nervously twisting a ring on her finger. She chewed on her lip and shook her head. "Her father couldn't deal with it. He got remarried in the spring, and his new wife just became tired of it all. We were just at our wits' end. You know how she was when she was here. She'd stand at the twenty-four-seven store, shouting at the boys who passed by in their cars. Some of them were not even boys . . . they were men."

Abel fell silent. He kept seeing the little girl on the dark street. He had worried about her. Ernesto Sandoval's mother had taken her home one night. Everybody had worried about her.

"She'd usually come home after a few weeks," Elena went on. "She'd clean up and, you know, my ex-husband said she'd seem all right. I wasn't living there then. I was in Las Vegas with my boyfriend. Sometimes Sarah would call me . . . but usually not. And then she didn't come home for a long time. My ex-husband called me, and . . . well, they found her in a ravine. She had overdosed."

Overdosed. Why wasn't Abel surprised at that? "That poor girl," was all he could think.

"When she was in my house," Elena continued, "she sometimes got at my pain medication. I take a lot of medication for my stress headaches and my nerves, and sometimes she'd steal some. But she never did hard drugs, not that I ever knew anyway. They said she didn't suffer or anything. She probably just lay down there and went to sleep."

Abel couldn't say anything. He just looked at the woman.

"She's buried in a small village in Mexico," Elena went on. She might have been talking to herself as much as to anyone else. She was staring out the store window. "My ex-husband's parents live there. It seemed a good place for her. I was just so upset for several months that I feared I'd never be happy again. Then Carl got me through it. He's such a wonderful man. I'm excited about life again. I wasn't sure there could be life after the death of a child, especially since I loved her so much. No mother ever loved a child more than I loved Sarah . . . but love is not enough. That's what they say."

Elena seemed to be coming out of a trance. She turned her head sharply toward Abel. The she glanced out at a red sports car, and she smiled brightly. "Anyway, there's Carl now!" She hurried out of the store.

Abel looked questioningly at Hector Ponce. He merely shrugged and said, "I thought it best to say nothing."

CHAPTER SIX

He had just one day left to go. Abel Ruiz had to work this afternoon at the doughnut shop, and then he was done. He'd been breaking in his replacement for the past week and a half, a sixteen-year-old junior from Cesar Chavez High School. This was Richie's first job. In Richie's excited eagerness to do a good job, Abel saw himself when he first started working here. Abel told Hector Ponce that Richie was going to be an excellent employee. He was quick, friendly, and enthusiastic.

But all during his classes, Abel had only one thought: Today would probably be the last time he would ever see Claudia Villa. Since she didn't go to Chavez High but to that private school, they wouldn't run into each other. After today, they would meet only by coincidence. Perhaps she'd be driving by in a car or something like that.

Abel was surprised by how much their breakup still hurt. He always disliked Clay Aguirre because he was such a jerk and a bully. But now he felt a little sorry for him. Clay had been with Naomi Martinez for a long time. Even though it was Clay's own fault that he lost her to Ernesto Sandoval, he had to feel awful. Clay probably loved Naomi in his own selfish way. When he was rude and mean to her, he didn't think anything of it. Clay had even hit Naomi. That was inconceivable behavior to Abel. Then, suddenly, she was gone. Abel now understood, as he never did before, why Clay took so long to heal.

Abel had nothing to be ashamed of in how he treated Claudia. He hadn't been rude and disrespectful to her, as Clay had been to Naomi. Abel had loved and treasured Claudia the best way he knew how.

He searched his memories for something he might have done to hurt her. But there was nothing. She just found someone she liked better. It was as simple as that.

Sadly, that conclusion confirmed in Abel's mind something he'd long feared about himself. He was a boring loser. He wasn't the sort of guy who could keep a classy chick like Claudia interested for the long haul. Abel's mother reinforced that fear. She always compared him to Tomás, his brother. Tomás had all the chicks he wanted and then some.

When Abel and Claudia first started dating, Abel felt as though he'd stumbled into a magic kingdom with fairy dust all over. Then, suddenly and predictably, the whole thing burst like a colorful soap bubble, leaving nothing but sadness.

During these past two weeks, Abel had done pretty much what Paul Morales had told him to do. He'd been calm and polite, and he'd never let Claudia see him bleed. This afternoon and evening would be the final chapter in that ordeal. Abel felt a lump in his throat, but he swallowed hard. He drove his VW Jetta over to Elena's Donut Shop, his jaw set. Paul was right. He'd be more of a man once this was over. He'd look back on it all and be proud of himself. He didn't whine and ask Claudia why she had dumped him, or worse, plead with her to come back. He didn't do any of those things, and he felt better for it. But it still hurt. This afternoon and evening, it would hurt more than ever.

When Abel entered the shop, Claudia took a long look at him. Abel thought he saw sadness in her eyes. Was she having second thoughts? Was the new relationship rocky already? Was Victor Toro already a disappointment? Or did she just feel bad about what she had done to a nice guy? Claudia was a nice, kindhearted girl. She probably felt awful that she had dumped Abel. Abel could only imagine what it'd be like if he'd met another girl that he liked better than Claudia, and he had to cut her loose. Not that it would have ever happened. But if it had, Abel thought he would feel terrible just looking at Claudia and knowing how she felt.

"Hi, Abel," Richie greeted. "I guess I'm flying solo after tonight. But I had the best coach in the world." Richie seemed a little nervous.

"You'll do fine," Abel assured him. "I was much worse than you when I started out here." Abel was lying just to make Richie feel better. Abel was pretty good early on. But this was the kid's first job, and he needed all the props he could get.

Richie's smile widened. "Thanks, man," he said.

Abel tried not to look at Claudia, but, every time he did, his heart ached a little more. He felt like crying, but he kept clinging to Paul's stern words. The shift was four hours, and Abel wasn't sure he could get through it.

Then, about fifteen minutes into the shift, Ernesto Sandoval and his two little sisters showed up. They hardly ever came into the doughnut shop, but here was Ernesto herding Katalina and Juanita to stools at the counter.

Abel didn't think this was any coincidence. Ernesto knew this was Abel's last night here. Ernesto was Abel's closest friend, and he knew what Abel was going through.

"Hi, Abel," Katalina chirped. "You gotta come to our house again and cook one of those wonderful dinners. I mean, Mom's a good cook, but you're like amazing!"

"You're the best cook in the whole world," Juanita agreed. "I can't wait to see you on TV like all those famous chefs."

"Thanks," Abel responded. They were such cute little girls, so full of energy and sweetness. Abel couldn't remember when Penelope was like that. She probably was before she became a teenager, he thought.

"I want a doughnut with jelly inside," Katalina said.

"Me too, me too," Juanita chimed in. "That one there in the middle of the tray, the big one."

"I guess I'll have one of those too," Ernesto said. "I'm in training on the track team, and Coach Muñoz wants me eating only healthy food. But what he doesn't know won't hurt him, right?"

"Abel," Katalina piped up, her mouth full of her jelly doughnut, "Alfredo just cries and cries. I never knew a baby could be such a pest!"

Abel had to smile in spite of his sadness. "He'll get better when he's a little older," he assured her.

"I don't know how Mama stands him," Juanita commented, wrinkling her nose. She had jelly all over her chin. "Mama just coos to him and laughs. She acts like she's not bothered when she has to change him a million times a day. But she must be pretending, because she even has to get up in the middle of the night!"

"Moms love their children a lot," Abel explained. "Even when they're a big bother. I guess moms can't help it."

"Papa too," Katalina noted. "Sometimes he gets up in the middle of the night too. He carries Alfredo around and calls him *mi hijo* and sings him back to sleep."

Juanita giggled, "Papa doesn't sing too good, but usually Alfredo goes to sleep."

"Yeah," Ernesto remarked, "Alfredo has taken over the house all right. He's the king of the *casa*. You know, Abel, something really hilarious happened last Sunday when Mom's mother came to visit. You know, Grandma Vasquez wanted Mom to be a big CEO or something. Mom wasn't supposed to be, like Grandma says, 'just a wife and mother.' Anyway, there was Grandma ragging on Mom as usual about her miserable life and all the lost opportunities. How Mom's wasting her brilliant mind, and the kids are sucking up all her energy."

Ernesto took a nibble out of his dough-nut. "So all of a sudden," Ernesto went on, "Mom says, 'Look, Mom, how cute Alfredo is.' And she puts the baby on Grand-ma's lap, but that doesn't stop her. She just keeps going and going. Well, Alfredo must have had to go really bad. Grandma stops yakking in midsentence, looks down, and freaks. His diaper was like a broken dam. It was overflowing. I didn't know a baby's bladder could hold that much pee. She had on this lilac dress, and it was soaked!"

Richie, Hector Ponce, Claudia, and even Abel laughed. For just a few minutes, everything seemed all right. When Ernesto and his sisters finally left, Abel glanced at the clock. He had three hours to go.

Before long, Paul Morales and Cruz Lopez showed up, neither of them with a girlfriend. They had to be doing that on purpose, Abel thought. The two boys wore baggy clothes and hoodies. They'd been traveling around the *barrio* in Cruz's wild-looking van.

"Hey, homies," Abel hailed. "Don't do anything suspicious tonight dressed like that. The law's gonna come down on you like a cloudburst."

Paul looked at Cruz. "Is that dude insulting our apparel? I thought we looked so cool that we'd be welcome anywhere."

"Yeah," Cruz said, grinning. "I think the man is saying we might scare folks. Remember that picture of that dude down at the bank, caught on a camera? The one who tried to rob the joint but he got scared and ran?"

Paul laughed. "Yeah! The dude did sorta look like us, didn't he? Those creeps give hoodies a bad name."

"We need to get better threads, homie," Cruz declared. "Like maybe one of those Armani suits like they advertise in the ritzy mags."

"And watches too," Paul added.

"Guys our age don't wear watches," Cruz said. "We got cells, right?"

"But dude," Paul objected, "did you ever see one of those Rolex things with diamonds and stuff? I mean something like that would really decorate my wrist. Even the rattlesnake tattoo would jump for joy."

The two ordered crullers, and they all bantered with one other for about thirty minutes.

Abel sensed that Claudia was waiting for a quiet moment to say good-bye. Or maybe she wanted to say she was sorry that things hadn't worked out for them. Abel didn't want to have that conversation. It wouldn't make him feel any better, only worse. No matter what she said, it meant only that she didn't love Abel anymore. She'd found someone else she cared about more.

Abel had been doing well so far, largely due to his friends popping in. He was afraid to come face to face with Claudia for some maudlin farewell. That would ruin everything. In the end, Claudia would see him bleed. Now, more than anything else, Abel did not want that to happen. He had his pride. He didn't want to lose that too. He'd lost the girl he loved, but he still had his pride.

Then Dom Reynosa and Carlos Negrete came into the shop. Abel had never seen them come in before. They'd been wannabe gangbangers, posting graffiti all over the *barrio*. Then Ernesto and his father got them back into Chavez High and got them to draw a beautiful mural at the school. They'd been dropouts, and now they were going to graduate. They were even getting paid to do neighborhood murals on the sides of buildings. When they saw the strobe lights of police cruisers, they didn't have to run anymore.

"Hey, Abel," Dom remarked, "understand you're gonna be the assistant chef at the Sting Ray, man." He took a stool and bought two chocolate doughnuts.

"Yeah, Pedro is sorta taking me on," Abel replied.

"Dude, I expect to see you makin' meals on the tube one of these days," Carlos told him, nibbling on a chocolate doughnut.

"Hey, man," Dom said, "you still like alt rock?"

"Sure," Abel responded.

"Remember that dude, Harry Castro, who used to hang out on Washington?" Dom asked. "He was up in Frisco for a while, and now he's back. He's making some cool music in a garage over on Adams. Me and Carlos are going over there for a while. When you're done here, why don't you join us? We could have a blast."

"Harry used to be the man," Abel declared.

"So just follow us over there when you get done here," Carlos suggested. "Be a good way to say good riddance to the smell of stale doughnuts!"

"You're on," Abel said.

Then it was time to go. Hector Ponce came out of the back room and held out his hand. "Abel, good luck to you. You were the best I ever had," he told the boy.

Abel glanced at the clock on the wall. Out of the corner of his eye, he saw Claudia edging closer. She wanted desperately to say something. Abel could tell she was trying to work up the courage to say something. She probably wanted at least to say good-bye.

"Need me to help clean up?" Abel asked Hector Ponce.

"Get out of here, *muchacho*," Hector commanded, laughing. He gave Abel a friendly punch. "Have a beautiful life!" He shoved a fifty dollar bill into Abel's hand. Then they high-fived each other.

Before he knew it, Abel was outside with the cool night air on his face. His heart was pounding. He jumped into the Jetta and started the engine. As he left the parking lot, he saw a panel of light. Claudia was coming out the back door of the shop and moving toward his car. Abel followed his friends out of the lot, toward Adams Street. He never slowed down. He never looked back.

If he had, he would have seen Claudia running to catch him before he was gone into the darkness.

As he drove toward where the alt band was performing, Abel got the picture.

Tonight didn't just happen. His friends, his homies, they all knew what was going down. They knew Abel was brokenhearted and sick and that tonight would be torment. So they worked it out. They came in relays so that he'd never be alone with his demons.

And it worked. Claudia never saw Abel bleed.

They were all there in the empty warehouse on Adams Street: Ernesto and Paul, Cruz and Beto, Dom and Carlos, and Julio Avila. They'd brought cold drinks and hot burritos from Hortencia's. They listened to music, ate and drank, and talked about old times until eleven thirty. Then, before heading home, Abel went to each of his friends for a fist bump and a hug.

Liza Ruiz was up when her son came home, sitting in the living room. Ordinarily she would have demanded to know why he was so late. She would have berated him for worrying her. But tonight she said in an almost calm voice, "*Mi hijo*, I was worried about you. Is everything all right?"

"Yeah, Mom," Abel responded. "I got together with my friends after work. We listened to this little alt rock band we like. It sorta helped me, you know . . ."

Liza Ruiz came over to her son and put her hands on his shoulders. She knew what tonight had been about. She knew what he had faced. "Now it's over. It will get better, Abel."

"Yeah," Abel mumbled.

"What did she say?" Mom asked. "Did she explain at all what happened?"

"A lot of my friends came in, Mom," Abel explained. "That four-hour shift went really fast. They were great. Ernie, Paul, Cruz, Dom, Carlos. They were there for me. It was good. I got the best homies in the *barrio*, Mom."

"But what did *she* say?" Mom persisted, her eyes wide. This girl had hurt her son. Abel didn't deserve to be hurt. Liza Ruiz did not understand why it had happened. In her mind, her second son was not as bright and handsome as her firstborn, Tomás. But she loved Abel as much, or even more, because he needed more love. She felt sorry for him. He was a good boy. The girl could not have found a finer young man with so good a heart, with so much honor and integrity. Why had she done such a thing? There had to be a reason.

"She didn't say anything, Mom," Abel answered. "I didn't want to talk to her, so I left really fast. She told me once what happened. She went for another guy. That's all there is to it. I didn't want to say good-bye to her. It was better how it went down. It was good, real good. My homies took care of me."

"Don't always call your friends that, Abel," Mom scolded. "It makes you sound like a gangbanger."

"Now that's more like you, Mom," Abel thought to himself. Out loud, he told his mother, "We all use that word, Mom. In the *barrio,* we call our friends homies 'cause they live near us. Just go look in the cemetery where a young guy is buried.

124

The stone'll say "home boy." It means he belongs here. I'm proud to be a home boy. There's not a guy living anywhere in the best neighborhood in the world, like up in Beverly Hills or up the coast in La Jolla— nowhere—who has better friends than I got right here in the *barrio*. I love these guys."

"So then she didn't even say good-bye?" Mom clung to her desire to know more, to understand.

"I told you, Mom, I didn't want that," Abel insisted. "What would it have meant? A lot of garbage is all. A lot of phony junk she didn't even mean. People saying stuff they're expected to say even though they don't mean it. Who needs that?"

Abel found himself having a meaningful conversation with his mother. He was trying to make her understand how he felt.

He went on. "My buddy, Paul Morales, he got it. He told me what I needed to do, and he was dead on. He told me to stay cool and not to let her see me bleed. That's what

I did, Mom. Yeah, I hurt inside. I ache, and tonight I'll probably cry. But it'll be in the dark, and nobody'll see me. She won't see it. She never heard me whine or saw me break, Mom. That means a lot to me. She never saw me bleed. I'm proud of that."

Liza Ruiz stood there in silence for a moment. Then she put her arms around her son and kissed him on the cheek. "I love you very much, Abel. I love you with all my heart. I'm proud of you too. You went through a tough time, and you handled it like a man. You're more *macho* than your father, *mi hijo*. I think that even Tomás could not have handled something like this as well as you did. I want you to know that I'm proud of you, and I love you."

"Love you too, Mom," Abel responded. "And . . . uh . . . thanks."

"Thanks for what?" Mom asked. "For loving you? I'm a mother. I have no choice."

"No," Abel explained. "I'm not thanking you for that. It's just that I think this is the first time in my life that you ever said

I did something better than Tomás could. That means a lot, Mom."

Abel went down the hall and went into his bedroom, closing the door gently after himself. He showered and got into his pajamas. He turned out the light before lying down.

Abel had told himself that Claudia's pretty face would fade slowly from his memory. His memory of her would blur like a very bright photograph that loses its sharpness over the years. Her beautiful eyes would become blurry, and he would forget the dimple in her chin. Recalling the special little inflections in her voice when she was very happy or excited would become harder and harder.

It would not hurt tomorrow as much as it hurt tonight, Abel told himself. And the night after that, it would hurt less. Abel told himself that, and he hoped it was true because right now he was hurting an awful lot.

Lying in the dark, Abel felt relieved that the two weeks at the doughnut shop were over. He had dreaded every day, and he had really dreaded tonight, the last day. He thought that, if he could not hold it together, he would lose it tonight. If the guys hadn't showed up, distracting him, one after another, he was pretty sure he would have come unglued. He would have looked over at Claudia and crumbled. Then all his brave efforts would have failed.

Tomorrow Abel would go to the Sting Ray and throw himself, heart and soul, into his work. For him, cooking was what liquor or sports or even drugs were for some. When he was chopping, mixing, tasting, and inhaling the aromas, the world—whether good or bad—receded. He was grateful for that.

CHAPTER SEVEN

Around the middle of the next week, Ernesto Sandoval caught up with Abel between classes. Ernesto asked, "How's it going at the Sting Ray, Abel?"

"It takes some getting used to working more time there," Abel responded. "I'm doing stuff I never did before. I'm working with shrimp and lobster tails, and I even go down to the fish market and buy stuff. I like it, though. The customers are mostly rich, and they demand the best. It's not like at Hortencia's. If the burritos aren't up to snuff, who complains? It's different for the rich."

Ernesto laughed. "Remember junior English when we were studying F. Scott

Fitzgerald and Ernest Hemingway? Didn't Fitzgerald say the rich were different from the rest of us?"

"Yeah, and Hemingway said, 'Yeah, they got more money.' But it's more than that. It's in their gut, man," Abel replied.

"See how much we remember from Ms. Hunt's class?" Ernesto said. "And when we were in there, we thought it was all a big waste of time."

Then he said, "How's Penelope doing? Still texting twenty-four-seven?"

"Mom is looking over her shoulder a lot," Abel explained. "I clued Mom in on some of the Internet lingo. When Penny hits 'NP' now, Mom knows she's telling whoever she's talking to that a nosy parent is nearby. Mom usually ends the conversation right then and there. Penny's getting kinda rebellious. I never was like that when I was fourteen. I was a wimp. Maybe that's one of my problems. Girls are turned off by wimps."

"Hey, man, you're no wimp," Ernesto protested. "You can't be a wimp and handle things the way you did with Claudia."

But Ernesto had another question. "You want to bring someone to the homecoming dance?"

Abel shrugged. "I don't know anybody. I don't even think I want to go. I'm not looking for a girlfriend, man. No way."

"There's a girl I know who really wants to go, but she doesn't have a boyfriend," Ernesto explained. "I don't know if you have any classes with her. She's in my AP American History, and she's really nice, but shy. She's not into social stuff, but the other day she told me she wished she could go to the homecoming dance. She said she'd even go with her brother if she had a brother."

As they walked to their classes, Abel glanced over at his friend. Indecision was in his eyes.

Ernesto continued. "If you'd be willing to take her, it would be a nice thing,

131

Abel. No big deal. She's not looking for a relationship—just going to the dance and seeing Yvette and Phil crowned. You know, some dancing and stuff. She said she'd never been to anything all through high school. Now pretty soon high school is over for us seniors. It would mean a lot to her."

Abel shrugged. "I guess it'd be okay. She'll probably hate me 'cause most girls do. But you say she doesn't care who takes her to the dance just so she can go? Then I guess I'm the guy."

"Great!" Ernesto said. "Her name is Bianca Marquez. She's tall, just a little bit shorter than you. She's a pretty girl, but she's too thin. She's got some problems."

"I guess we all do," Abel remarked.

At his AP class, Ernesto sat down next to Bianca before Mr. Bustos got there.

"You know what, Bianca?" he asked. "The other day you said you'd really like to go to the homecoming dance, right?"

132

"Yeah, I've never been to anything like that," Bianca replied.

"I got a good friend here at Chavez, Abel Ruiz," Ernesto told her. "I'm telling you, Bianca, he's the nicest guy in the world. I'm telling you, he's my best friend. He's as close as a brother to me. He isn't going with anybody right now. I told him there's this nice, pretty girl who'd just like to go to the dance, and he said he'd like that too. So, you game?"

"Has he ever *seen* me?" Bianca asked. "I mean, I'm not Miss Universe."

"Bianca, you're a hot chick," Ernesto assured her.

"Oh, Ernie, that's not true," Bianca objected. "Boys don't like me at all."

"Bianca, that's because you look sort of sad and down all the time," Ernesto replied. "You don't smile much. Guys like chicks who smile and laugh. You know, bubbly types. But the good thing about Abel is, he's kind of a quiet guy too. He's been going through some hard times, and

133

he's ready for a nice, quiet chick like you. I think you guys would be perfect for each other. You know, just to have a fun night. Nobody looking to impress anybody."

Bianca smiled. "You're something else, Ernie. You're all the time trying to fix the world, aren't you? Most people see a problem, and they walk away from it. You pitch in and try to make everything better."

"How about if you and me go the coffee shop across the street for frappés after classes today," Ernesto suggested. "While we're there, I'll text Abel to come join us. You guys can check each other out. If you think he's okay, you can make your plans. Because Abel's good to go, Bianca."

"Let me think about it," Bianca replied. "I'll let you know after class."

"Okay," Ernesto agreed, heading for his usual place in class. He wanted to do a kindness for Bianca. The chick seemed so lonely. But Ernesto had another motive too. He wanted to ease Abel back into the swing of hanging with girls. He didn't seem to be getting over Claudia.

Mr. Bustos came bounding into the room, eager to teach. He was one of the most enthusiastic teachers Ernesto ever had.

In an earlier class, Bianca had made a mistake in front of everybody. She'd said that Thomas Jefferson had opposed the French Revolution because it was so violent and bloody. Rod Garcia, whom Ernesto had beaten out for senior class president, snickered at Bianca's mistake, adding to her humiliation. Now Bianca said nothing at all during class discussions, and that would cost her points for her grade.

Ernesto had spent a lot of time studying with Bianca over the past week. They spent a whole hour on the topic of today's discussion—the relationship between Aaron Burr and Alexander Hamilton. So Bianca seemed to have a good grasp of the material. Ernesto was hoping she would rise above her fears and contribute to the class today.

"So," Joaquin "Quino" Bustos lectured, "we have Aaron Burr, a very illustrious gentleman with a shining war record from the Revolutionary War. He'd been a colonel and then vice president of the United States under Jefferson. Then there is a falling-out between Jefferson and Burr, no? So what does Jefferson do?"

From the corner of his eye, Ernesto could see that Bianca was struggling for the courage to answer. But she was hesitating. Her fear took over. She knew the answer, but she remembered her last mistake. Rod Garcia took the question by default.

"Jefferson dropped Burr for consideration for the next election. Burr would not be on the ticket for vice president," Garcia answered.

"Yes!" Bustos almost shouted. "And Burr is a proud man. He does not take kindly to being shunted aside. He begins to deeply resent Jefferson and the power of the Virginia Republicans. Burr now wants to become governor of New York. So we have a plot forming, a serious plot that threatens the very existence of this fledgling United States of America. What is Burr plotting?"

Bianca looked panic-stricken, but she raised her hand. Ernesto's heart began to pound. With all his will, he tried to empower her.

"Yes, Bianca?" Mr. Bustos said.

"The New England Federalists wanted a Northern Confederacy of New England and New York," Bianca stammered. "Their plan was to secede from the Union so that the Southerners, led by Virginia, had no more say over them. It would have broken up the country."

"Exactly!" Mr. Bustos cried. "And what did Alexander Hamilton, the Federalist, think of this plot?"

"Hamilton wouldn't have anything to do with it," Bianca answered, her voice stronger. "Hamilton undermined Burr's plans and got him defeated for governor of New York. That ended the secession conspiracy."

"Precisely!" Mr. Bustos thundered.

Ernesto felt like applauding. Bianca had risen above her timidity and her fears, and she had triumphed. All those hours Ernesto spent with her had paid off.

When the class ended, Bianca quickly came to Ernesto's side. "Thanks for all those study sessions, Ernie. It made the difference," she told him.

"You got the brains, Bianca," Ernesto complimented her. "It's all there. We just stirred it up a bit."

Ernesto stood face to face with her in the hallway. He was waiting for an answer from Bianca. "So?" he asked.

"I guess if that guy Abel can stand me, I'd like a shot at going to the homecoming dance, Ernie," Bianca replied with an uncertain smile.

Meanwhile, Abel wished he hadn't agreed to go to the coffee shop. He didn't want to meet this girl he didn't even know. He had no appetite whatsoever for taking her to the dance. The more he thought about it, the sorrier he was that he'd agreed.

He hoped that Ernesto would text him to say the idea had gone down, that the girl had chickened out.

But if that didn't happen, Abel would do his duty. Ernesto had had his back too many times, Abel wouldn't dream of shooting down one of Ernie's good-guy projects. Abel could see that Ernesto really wanted to help this chick—Bianca.

Abel got Ernesto's text.

"Meet us at the coffee shop," it said.

"Oh man!" Abel groaned. He texted back, "On the way." He didn't have the heart to back out, so he crossed the street, clinging to one last hope. Maybe this Bianca chick would take one look at him and back out. Maybe she wouldn't want to go to the homecoming dance after all.

At the coffee shop, Abel saw Ernesto in a booth with a girl who had long, dark hair. She turned her head slightly, and Abel was surprised at how pretty she was. He didn't expect that. A chick who looked that good shouldn't be having trouble lining up

139

a date. But then he remembered Ernesto saying how shy she was. Abel knew what that was like. Shyness had a way of ruining everything.

Ernesto spotted Abel and waved him over. "Over here, dude!" he called in his jolly voice. Abel walked over and Ernesto said, "Bianca, this is my best *amigo*, Abel Ruiz. Abel, this is Bianca Marquez, a really nice girl."

As Abel sat down and muttered a greeting, Ernesto began raving about his good qualities. "When I came to Cesar Chavez High last year as a junior, Bianca, I didn't know anybody. I felt like I was an alien who just stepped off a UFO. I thought I'd never make a friend, and this guy here made it his project to help me fit in. He was an instant friend. I'm telling you, Bianca, I couldn't have made it without him."

Abel looked at Bianca. She was even prettier close up than she'd been when he first spied her from the door. "He's making too much of what I did," Abel protested.

"This dude had everybody loving him in about twenty-four hours."

"No way!" Ernesto insisted. "Bianca, you've got no idea of what it was like for me. I was coming down from LA to a strange high school. Some of the guys actually hated me. I was scared of them. But you know what happened? Abel got all his homies to come over and stand with me. Right then and there, I knew I'd found a home."

"That's really nice," Bianca commented.

She was looking at Abel now with her big, soft eyes. Abel thought she was probably thinking, "How can I go to the homecoming dance with such a dumb-looking jerk? How did I get into this mess?" Abel wished he could drop through the floor. But he said, "So, Bianca, it'd maybe be fun if we went to the homecoming dance, huh?"

"Yeah," Bianca replied. "I've never been. I heard about the theme music, 'Estrellas fugaces,' and I just love that song. Shooting stars! And I pictured the guy all fixed up sort of magical. It seemed

141

so cool. My mom said homecoming dances are a big waste of time, but I always wanted to go at least once. Now that I'm a senior, well, I guess it's now or never."

"Yeah," Abel agreed. "Let's go then. I've never been to one either. I got this older brother, Tomás. When he was here at Chavez, he was homecoming king. Can you believe it? This guy is good-looking and smart, and everybody loved him. I never liked him too much myself."

Bianca laughed at that. Ernesto had never seen her really laugh. Her laughter did marvels for her face. She had dimples in her cheeks, and her eyes shone when she laughed.

"We live in a condo over on Cardinal Street . . . 330 Cardinal Street," Bianca told him.

"Great," Abel replied. "That's where I'll pick you up."

When Abel got home from school, he saw Penelope texting again. She was sitting on the couch in the living room, texting like mad.

"Penny," Abel commented, "I bet you send ten thousand texts a month."

"So what?" Penelope snapped. "I've got a lot of friends, and we need to stay connected."

"Yeah," Abel responded, "every one of them needs to know what you're doing every minute of the day. Like, 'Hey, I'm polishing my toenails. Now I'm brushing my teeth. Uh-oh, I have to comb my hair now.' "

"Oh, give it a rest, Abel," Penelope growled. "You're just jealous that you don't have as many friends as I do."

"I don't want a bunch of creepy people keeping tabs on me all the time," Abel objected. "It makes me tired just thinking about it. 'Hey, guess what, Ernie? I'm having a can of soda!' 'Hey, know what I'm doing now? I'm changing my socks, dude.' "

"Oh, shut up!" Penelope snarled. She was in a bad mood ever since that weirdo she met online vanished from her life. She still didn't know that Abel and his homies had scared the wits out of him.

Abel's mother came into the living room. "Penelope Ruiz, put that phone away and do your homework! Do you hear me?"

Abel thought his mother needed to hear some good news. She'd really been worried about him since Claudia Villa went away. "Mom," he announced, "I'm going to the homecoming dance at Chavez."

Liza Ruiz brightened immediately. She even ignored the fact that Penelope was paying no attention to her and was continuing to text.

"Oh, Abel, that's wonderful," Mom exclaimed. "You've met a girl already!" When Mom got excited, she sounded like a sixteen-year-old girl. Her voice went up an octave, and she giggled out the syllables.

"It's no big deal, Mom," Abel replied. "But Ernie knows this girl who really wants

144

to go to the homecoming dance, so I'm taking her. I mean, it's more like a good deed, you know?"

"Is she nice, Abel?" Mom continued in her little girl voice. "I bet she's pretty."

"She's okay," Abel admitted.

Penelope briefly looked up from her texting. "I bet she's a bow-wow," she remarked.

"Penny!" Mom scolded. "That is so unkind. Not every girl can be stunningly beautiful, but there's something appealing about everyone. I don't know what's the matter with you, Penelope. Your brother Tomás is such a nice, kind person. He would never describe a girl as a dog even if she wasn't very attractive."

"Not in front of you, no," Penelope admitted. "But he said lots of things worse than calling a girl a dog."

"I don't believe it," Mom cried indignantly. "Tomás isn't that kind of person."

Penelope sneered. Abel sank into a leather chair and pretended to be studying his iPhone. But he was immensely enjoying the conversation.

Penelope was in a spiteful mood. Finally, something distracted her from texting. She dropped her hands into her lap and spoke directly to her mother.

"I remember when Tomás was going to Chavez," the girl began. "He'd be standing around with his friends in the parking lot, and sometimes I'd come over from middle school. Tomás and the other guys would be rating the girls as they went by. They'd call the ugly girls bulldogs and the real pretty ones poodles. They'd be laughing and slapping their thighs like crazy. I guess they thought it was funny, but it was pretty gross."

"Penelope," Mom responded, "I'm really hurt that you're telling lies about your brother like this." Mom seemed tearful.

Most of the time, Abel didn't like his sister much, though he did love her and he was fiercely protective of her. He went nuts when that creep was picking her up in his

146

car. But ordinarily, Abel stayed clear of the arguments between his mother and sister. Still, right now he wanted to come to Penelope's defense.

"No, Mom, Penny's right," he told Mom. "I'd often hear Tomás and his friends sitting out there on the sidewalk, rating the girls in the *barrio*. There was this one poor girl who was tall and skinny. They called her whippet; you know after that big ugly dog, with the skinny head and the long . . ."

"Oh!" Mom cried, "I don't want to hear another word!" She turned on her heels and hurried into the kitchen.

Penelope giggled. "Mom lives in a dream world when it comes to Tomás," she chuckled. "I guess pretty much when it comes to everything. I was texting and she was hovering around. I quick typed in PAL, and she asked me what that meant. I told her it meant 'party at Larry's.' She bought it! She didn't have a clue it meant 'parents are listening,' of course. And then me and Dani were joking about what we'd like to do with a boy. Mom saw me type in KOC, and she didn't know it meant 'kiss on the cheek.' I said it meant 'keep on chilling.'"

"But you don't have a boyfriend, right, Penny?" Abel asked.

"I do sorta, but he doesn't know it," Penelope responded. "He's such a wimp. Fourteen-year-old boys are wimps!"

"Yeah," Abel advised. "Stick with the wimps, girl."

"Abel, you can tell me the truth," his sister told him. "Is this girl you're taking to the homecoming dance a real dog?"

"No. She's pretty," Abel replied. "But I don't have any feelings for her. I'm just interested in my job now. I'm not getting mixed up with another girl like I did with Claudia."

"You still feel bad about her, huh?" Penelope asked, her usually snide face appearing to be genuinely sympathetic.

"Yeah," Abel said. "You can't just blow something like that away. She was a big part of my life, and now there's a hole there." Abel was surprising himself that he was sharing so much of his deeply personal feelings with his snotty little sister.

Penelope stuck her iPhone into her pocket and got up. She walked over to where Abel was and sat on the arm of his chair. "I'm sorry, Abel. I'm really sorry," she told him. "You deserved better than what you got. Sometimes you make me sick, but you're a pretty nice brother. But it'll get better. Even though you're my brother, I think you're kinda cute. There'll be another chick."

Abel smiled at his little sister. Her consoling job done, she went right back to texting.

CHAPTER EIGHT

Abel Ruiz wasn't sure how he felt taking Bianca Marquez to the homecoming dance. Maybe it was too soon to be going anywhere with a girl. Maybe he'd take one look at this tall stranger, and the ache over losing Claudia would get worse. But he had promised, and he wouldn't go back on his word.

On the night of the homecoming dance, Abel got dressed, and his mother made a fuss over him. She kept telling him how handsome he looked. He bought a corsage for Bianca because that's what he was supposed to do.

Abel drove to the condo on Cardinal Street. The condos were new and very nice.

150

They were a far cry from the really elegant condos on the beach. But they were way better than the houses where Abel and his friends lived. And they were light years away from the rundown apartments on Starling and Oriole.

The Ruiz family had taught Abel his manners well. So he parked the VW Jetta, went to the door, and rang the bell, corsage in hand.

A very thin, attractive woman answered. She looked as though she had probably had a face-lift. Her skin was very tight. She reminded Abel of a teacher he had once whose face was very taut. His mother told him she'd had "work done."

"You must be Abel Ruiz," the woman said. "Come in."

It was a lovely living room filled with modern furniture that Abel figured he'd better not sit on. Abel couldn't imagine flopping into one of the strange, elongated chairs. Liza Ruiz kept a nice house. But there was never any doubt that people

151

relaxed there and didn't worry too much about sagging cushions.

"Darling, Abel Ruiz is here," the woman called down the hall. Within a minute, Bianca appeared. She wore a pale green prom dress with one bare shoulder. She looked much thinner than she looked at school. At school, she usually wore pullovers with long sleeves. Now her long, skinny arms were startling.

"Hi, Abel," Bianca said, taking the corsage. "Oh, it's beautiful. Thank you. Will you pin it on, Abel?"

Abel kept trying not to look into the strange girl's face as he fumbled with the corsage. The creamy white flowers went well with her green dress. He finally got it fastened.

"We didn't think Bianca was going to the homecoming dance," the girl's mother remarked. "I never went to school dances at all, and neither did my husband. We just thought they were silly, I guess."

Then Abel saw a nervous-looking stout little man who sat at a computer. He was working diligently. He didn't even seem to notice Abel was in the room. It was Bianca's stepfather.

As Abel and Bianca went outside, she said, "My stepfather is very busy. He's always doing spreadsheets. Mom met him when they were both teaching at the community college. He's okay, but we don't have much of a relationship."

"Oh," Abel responded. He couldn't think of anything more profound to say.

"Thank you so much for taking me to the homecoming dance," Bianca said as she got in the car. "I really wanted to go."

"Ah sure," Abel replied. He felt tongue-tied. If she were Claudia, they'd be chattering away together by now. But Bianca held her hands on her lap and looked out the window. She wore a turquoise bracelet, and she twisted it nervously. Abel figured she was as ill at ease as he was.

Abel thought he might tell Bianca that he was an apprentice chef and that she looked like she didn't eat enough. But that would have been rude. Her weight was none of his business. So Abel just hoped that the night would pass quickly without any major disasters.

"Do you dance, Abel?" Bianca asked as they neared Cesar Chavez High School.

"No," Abel answered. "It seems sorta weird to me."

Bianca laughed. She didn't laugh often. Abel turned and looked at her, noticing that the laughter dimpled her cheeks. She went from being an attractive girl to a kind of hot chick.

Earlier that day, Cesar Chavez had played a great football game, beating long-time rival Wilson by two touchdowns. Clay Aguirre played a big part in the victory, and Abel had to grudgingly admit the guy was good.

During the homecoming festivities, Yvette Ozono and Phil Serra were crowned king and queen. Abel had never seen Yvette look so beautiful, even though she was crying. Phil Serra put his arm protectively around her.

"That's quite a story," Abel told Bianca. "That girl has come an awful long way."

"She's exquisite," Bianca commented.

When Abel and Bianca went in the gym, it looked like a fairyland. Little white lights, cleverly placed in the ceiling, were magical, even twinkling like stars. Ernesto Sandoval and the senior class advisor, Deprise Wilson, had arranged for an excellent DJ. The music mix was just right enough to satisfy all tastes, from alt rock to punk, from hip-hop and rap to reggae. Ms. Wilson had promised a special surprise tonight, and suddenly the DJ stopped the music. A tall, striking young man with a guitar appeared in the spotlight.

"It's Orlando Martinez," Carmen Ibarra gasped. The theme song of the homecoming was the song he had been singing on YouTube—"Estrellas fugaces." The whole

155

gym erupted in cheers and screams. Abel glanced over at Ernesto and Naomi Martinez, Orlando's sister. She was jumping up and down and screaming with the rest of the girls.

When Orlando finished the song, he came down and danced with his sister and several other girls. Then he escaped out a side door. He had to get back to Los Angeles for a gig with the Oscar Perez Latin Band he belonged to.

At the end of the dance, as Abel and Bianca left the gym, she was flushed with excitement. "Oh, I'm so glad we came!" she exclaimed. "It was so exciting. I thought it would be wonderful, but it was even better than I expected. And that singer! Wasn't he awesome?"

"Yeah, Naomi's brother," Abel agreed. "You know Naomi Martinez, don't you?"

"Yes, she's in two of my classes," Bianca answered. "She's really nice. She's Ernie's girlfriend. They're perfect together. Ernie is so lucky to have found her, and she's lucky to be with him. It's funny, isn't it, how things happen sometimes like that. Do you think it's just a coincidence, or is it fate?"

"I don't know," Abel replied blankly. He thought about Claudia. He was stunned with joy when he got together with her. He kept asking himself how he was so fortunate that a girl like Claudia would date him. And he never understood why. And then, when she left him, he was stunned with grief. He didn't understand that either.

When they got into the Jetta, Abel made a suggestion. "It's not so late. Want to stop at Hortencia's for something to eat?"

"Oh, I don't know," Bianca hesitated. "I've been eating too much lately. I'm scared to step on the scale."

"Uh, don't be scared, Bianca. Trust me," Abel insisted. "You don't weigh too much. We could just get a couple mini tacos. Hortencia makes the most amazing shrimp mini tacos."

157

"Mom always told me she was so overweight when she was a teenager that she wouldn't even wear a swimsuit. And I've got the same genes," Bianca objected.

"Your mom looks really thin now," Abel noted.

"Oh, she eats practically nothing," Bianca explained. "She weighs herself half a dozen times in a day."

They pulled into Hortencia's and found a table. Bianca looked at the mini shrimp tacos covered with tangy salsa.

"Oh!" Bianca remarked. "They look so good."

"Eat up, Bianca," Abel urged. He wolfed down two tacos, one after the other, and was going for a third.

When Bianca hesitated to take even a bite, Abel found the courage to say what was on his mind. "Listen, Bianca, don't take this wrong, okay? I hope I'm not talking out of turn or anything. But you don't look so good being as thin as you are. You'd look a lot better with a few extra pounds."

Bianca looked surprised, but she did eat two mini tacos. "I haven't tasted anything so good in ages," she announced.

When they were driving home, Abel felt he needed to say more to Bianca. "Our parents love us a lot," he began. "And they want good for us and stuff, but they're not always right, Bianca. I got good parents. I got a great mom, but she's always torn me down, you know? She loves me, but she always thought I was a big loser. She pitied me and didn't expect much from me. When I got this cooking thing going, she was sure I'd be a big flop."

Abel frowned at the memory and continued speaking. "She didn't even want me to invite our friends over to taste the first big meal I made. She said she'd be so embarrassed if it turned out bad. She was sure I'd screw up. But my friends, my homies, they stuck with me and gave me courage. Your mom seems like a great lady. But she's kinda got a problem if she's starving herself and weighing herself all day. Don't you think? It'd be a shame if her problem ruined your life, you know? The truth is, Bianca, girls look great with curves."

Bianca didn't say a word. Abel figured he'd blown the whole evening. He thought he'd hurt her feelings or something.

When they got to her condo, Abel walked her to the door. Bianca thanked him for taking her, and she said she had a wonderful time. Abel said he had a good time too, although he didn't. He had kept thinking about Claudia. When Bianca was inside the condo, Abel returned to his car. Bianca Marquez was a nice girl, but she was not Claudia. Abel wondered whether any girl could ever make him forget Claudia.

When Abel arrived at the Sting Ray the next Monday, somebody new was there, a girl with more black curls than he had ever seen, and bright, sparkling eyes. Pedro said, "Abel, this is my niece, Cassie Ursillo. She just turned eighteen. She graduated from Lincoln last year, and she wants to be a chef, like you. Cassie, this is Abel Ruiz. He is very good around food."

"Hi, Abel," Cassie said. "I'm good around food too. I'm a magician in the kitchen."

"Hi, Cassie," Abel responded. He thought she seemed very arrogant. His first impression was not good.

"I just have a sixth sense about seasonings," Cassie went on. "My father was a chef before he got sick and had to retire. He was the best chef on the West Coast. He taught me everything he knew. I can tell what little pinch of something will turn a good meal into a great one."

Abel thought to himself that the girl could use a little pinch of humility. "Seasoning is important," he agreed.

"It's everything!" Cassie declared in a strident voice that was already getting on Abel's nerves. "The wrong seasoning can destroy the best salmon or the choicest steak."

"We'll be featuring our shrimp Florentine tonight," Pedro directed. "So we need to get our ingredients lined up."

Cassie looked intently at Abel, "Is your father a chef too?"

"No," Abel answered. "He's a gardener."

Cassie looked shocked. "So where did you learn to cook?"

"I taught myself," Abel explained. "I read a lot and watched the chefs on the cooking channel on TV."

"Oh," Cassie said. "I'm in culinary school right now."

"Right after I graduate from Chavez I'll be going there," Abel replied. He had gone from being annoyed with Cassie Ursillo to disliking her intensely.

"Uncle Pedro," Cassie dictated, "we'll need red bell peppers and baby corn nuggets for the shrimp Florentine. And, of course, spinach leaves. I hope we have garlic salt."

"Of course," Pedro responded, smiling tolerantly.

"And tarragon leaves," Abel added, "fresh or dried."

"Oh, that's not necessary," Cassie said. "I know some people use them, but they're overrated."

"No way," Abel protested. "We've got to have them. They make all the difference."

"Where did you get that idea, Abel?" Cassie asked, sneering at him. "From one of those silly TV cooks? They don't know anything. They're hired because they're clowns, not because they really know cooking."

"Was Julia Child a clown?" Abel asked dryly.

"Oh, Abel," Cassie tossed her dark curls. "My father told me you can lose the tarragon leaves, and nobody'll even notice."

Abel looked at Pedro. "You got tarragon leaves?"

"Yeah," Pedro answered, "I got dried ones on hand."

"Okay," Abel suggested, "when we get the first order, let me do a shrimp Florentine

163

with tarragon leaves. Cassie can do hers without. Then you taste them, Pedro."

"That is so juvenile," Cassie snorted, but Pedro agreed.

Late in the afternoon, some customers ordered the shrimp Florentine stir-fry. Pedro stir-fired the shrimp for three minutes. Abel and Cassie added chopped red bell peppers, baby corn nuggets, spinach leaves, and garlic salt. Then Abel added tarragon leaves to one of the orders, while Cassie left it off hers. Pedro tasted the dishes just before they were served. He looked at Abel and directed, "Add the tarragon leaves."

Abel resisted the impulse to sneer at Cassie. Pedro could tell with one taste that the tarragon leaves added something special. After the couple finished their meal, they told Pedro it was the best shrimp Florentine they had ever tasted, even in San Francisco.

"She would have said the same thing if we'd of left out the stupid tarragon leaves," Cassie grumbled

"No," Pedro objected softly. "They added a special touch. Last month, we ran out of tarragon leaves, and the turkey rolls were very mediocre."

As the evening progressed, Cassie kept making small critical remarks to Abel. "You're chopping the garlic too fine," she snapped.

"I always do the cloves like this," Abel snapped back.

"My father said never to chop the garlic cloves too fine," Cassie insisted. Later she said, "Abel, you're not cubing the butternut squash right."

"This is how I do it for polenta," Abel replied. "And it works fine."

Abel had always enjoyed coming to the Sting Ray, but this night was turning out to be a trial. Cassie Ursillo had a contrary opinion on just about everything Abel did. Abel was hoping she wouldn't be around regularly.

After the restaurant closed down for the night, Pedro made coffee, and the staff unwound. Abel wanted to join the busboys at a nearby table. He didn't want any more contact with Cassie tonight. But before he could escape to the busboy table, Cassie grabbed his arm and steered him to her table. "We need to talk," she commanded.

Abel was expecting another critical tirade. Instead, Cassie said, "So you're a senior at Cesar Chavez High School."

"Yeah," Abel replied, steeling himself for an attack on the school. He expected her to say something critical about it. Maybe it was the worst high school in the country. Or more gangbangers went there than to any other school.

"I wanted to go there," Cassie admitted, surprising Abel. "But they foreclosed on our house, and we rented near Lincoln. So I had to go there. You got brothers and sisters, Abel?" She sipped her black coffee. Abel took cream and lots of sugar in his coffee.

"Got a younger sister and an older brother," Abel answered.

166

"I got two older sisters who lord it over me," the girl confided. "They try to anyway, but they don't get away with it. You know, I love old movies and old music. Nobody my age likes the kind of stuff I enjoy. I mean, I listen to singers who died before my *father* was born. Nobody has ever even heard of them. Do you like old stuff?"

"No, I like the music they're making now. I like alt rock and hip-hop and sometimes reggae if it's good," Abel said.

"I'm crazy about old movies," Cassie commented. "I hate the movies they're making now. I hate those special effects and all that stuff. You know who I *really* like from the old time days? I just love James Dean. I've got James Dean posters all over my room. Do you even know who he was, Abel?"

"Ah sure," Abel replied, feeling relieved that they could have a normal conversation. "He was that guy who made *Rebel Without a Cause*. I've seen that on TV. He died when my grandmother was young. She had a big crush on him."

"Yeah, he was really young when his car crashed, and he died. Oh wow, though," Cassie sighed. "There's never been anybody else like him."

The girl looked directly at Abel. "You know what, Abel? You've driven me nuts tonight because you're such a know-it-all."

She was so into herself that she didn't notice Abel nearly spit out his coffee. She just rattled on.

"There's one thing I need to tell you. You got James Dean eyes. It's the creepiest thing, but it's true. It just gives me the chills, but you got James Dean eyes. Did anybody ever tell you that before?"

CHAPTER NINE

On his way home from his shift at the Sting Ray, Abel felt very strange. Cassie Ursillo had bugged him all night, and he couldn't wait to get away from her. But then, as he was seething with resentment, she came at him out of left field. She said Abel had James Dean eyes! Abel never gave James Dean much thought, but he did know that the dude was pretty hot in his time. All the chicks went for him. Then he died in an auto crash when he was only twenty-four. After that, he became one of those icons who appear from time to time in the entertainment world. Like Elvis Presley and Marilyn Monroe, he died before he got old but stayed forever young and attractive in people's imagination. James Dean, though, was really, *really* young, and he'd been a symbol of youthful angst and rebellion.

"James Dean eyes? A dork like me?" Abel thought.

When Abel got home, his mother was checking her e-mail. She didn't go online often, and then she deleted almost everything. "Hi, Mom," he said. "Anything interesting?"

"No, the usual junk," Mom grumbled. "How did it go tonight, honey?"

"Good," he sighed, "'cept the boss's niece works there now, and she's a pain. She was second-guessing everything I did, and she was wrong too. What an arrogant pest."

"Abel, if your boss has hired his niece, then you have to be careful. Don't get on her bad side," Mom warned.

"I'm sticking to what I know needs to be done," Abel said. Then he changed the subject. "Mom, did you ever see a James Dean movie?"

Mom laughed. "Of course. He died before I was born, but I've seen his movies on TV. I must have seen *Rebel Without a Cause* ten times. He was so good. I even had a poster of him in my room when I was a kid. He had this haunting beauty about his face. He looked so sad. You just wanted to put your arms around him and comfort him. Why do you ask, Abel?"

"This girl, the boss's niece," Abel answered, "she said something really stupid. I guess maybe she was making fun of me or something."

Mom got up from the computer and walked over to him. She looked concerned. She was always a little worried about what would happen to her second son. To her, Abel had none of the winning qualities of his older brother. "What did the girl say, *mi hijo*?" Mom asked gently.

Abel swallowed. He was a little bit sorry he'd even brought it up. "She said I had eyes like James Dean. I know she was making a joke, but she looked real serious.

171

She asked if anybody had ever told me that before." Abel looked at his mother. He expected her to laugh.

But Liza Ruiz reached up, touched her son's face, and looked into his eyes. "Oh *Santo Dios*!" she whispered. "I see it. It's true. That same vulnerable look, the sad dark eyes. This girl must be very perceptive, Abel."

Abel shrugged.

"Abel, James Dean died so long ago," Mom said, turning then and going to her bedroom. "It's amazing this young woman would even remember him." In her room, she rustled around in a trunk for a few minutes. Then she reappeared with a shiny publicity photo of James Dean. "This belonged to my mother, your grandmother. She wrote right here on the picture—'James Dean, who died on my 21st birthday. Sleep in peace, Jimmy.'"

Abel took the photograph and looked at it. He didn't think he looked much like James Dean, except maybe, yes, around the eyes. Abel handed the picture back to his mother.

"It was a compliment, Abel," Mom told him. "The girl gave you a compliment."

Abel had spent every night since he lost Claudia thinking about her. He recalled their dates, the walks they took, the cute things she did. But tonight he was thinking about Cassie. He couldn't get over how angry she'd made him by questioning everything he did. Even though Abel was reliving the hard time Cassie gave him, it felt good to fall asleep not thinking about Claudia.

The next time Abel went to work at the Sting Ray, Cassie wasn't there. Abel breathed a sigh of relief.

"Cassie has classes at the culinary school today," Pedro explained. "Listen, Abel, I'm sorry about how she was hassling you. She's quite a handful, but she's a pretty good cook, and she's my sister's kid. They're really up against it, so what can I do?"

"It's okay," Abel said. "I can hold my own."

"Yeah!" Pedro responded grinning. "You sure can. And you were right too. I don't know where you get all the know-how you got, *muchacho*, but you're a natural chef."

"Cassie said her father was this big shot chef," Abel noted. "How come they're into hard times?"

Pedro looked sad. "My brother-in-law was a top-notch chef, but a gambler too. Made good money, spent more. They lost their house, had to move to a little apartment. And then the poor guy had a stroke. He's only in his fifties, but he acts like he's eighty. My sister has to work in retail to keep the family going."

"That's too bad," Abel commented, feeling sorry for Cassie. But still, she didn't have to second-guess every little thing he did.

Abel helped prepare the special of the evening—red snapper teriyaki. It was one of his favorite entrees. He made it for Ernesto

Sandoval and his family once, and they never stopped raving about it. Abel cut the red snapper into one-inch pieces and then prepared the asparagus, the red bell pepper, and teriyaki baste and glaze. The noodles were ready to go. When people started ordering, Abel and another cook stir-fried the snapper for two minutes and added the vegetables to serve with the noodles.

In the middle of the evening, Pedro gave Abel a thumbs-up. The snapper was a hit with the customers.

While walking home, Abel felt strangely restless. So he did what his friend Ernesto did when he couldn't get to sleep. He went for a walk. So he turned left instead of right—the way home. It was ten thirty, and not many people were on the street. A strong wind had blown all day. The sidewalk and streets were littered with dead fronds from the lanky Washington palms that lined most of the bird streets.

Abel pulled a couple of the larger palm fronds out of the street so there wouldn't be

175

an accident. When he straightened up, he saw a tall girl wearing a hoodie coming from the opposite direction. Abel thought it was a bad idea for a girl to be out at night alone.

When Abel got closer to the girl, he recognized Bianca Marquez. She smiled and remarked, "Looks like I'm not the only night owl, huh?"

"Kinda dangerous for a chick to be walking alone in the dark, Bianca," Abel advised.

"Oh, I'm okay," Bianca said. "It's such a beautiful night. Look at that big full moon. And the stars. I can pick out all the constellations. My father taught me to find them when I was very small."

"That was nice," Abel replied. "You still see your dad?"

"Yeah, a couple times a year," Bianca answered. "He lives in London with his new wife."

"So how old were you when your folks split?" Abel asked.

"Eleven. It was hard at first. But it got better," Bianca said softly. "My stepfather ısn't bad. He really appreciates Mom. He's always bringing her flowers, taking her out to dinner. She's happy with him I think."

Bianca swallowed hard. Abel could see it was hard for her to talk about her family situation. He felt sorry that he'd asked.

But for some reason, even with a sad look on her face, Bianca continued talking. "I didn't blame my parents for the divorce. Mom says she let herself go, and Dad met this really hot office assistant. Now she's real careful to look great all the time. I guess things happen for the best. What do they call it—karma?"

"I'll walk you home, Bianca," Abel offered.

"Oh, you don't need to. I walk at night all the time," Bianca said.

"I'd feel better," Abel insisted.

Neither of them said much while they walked to Bianca's condo and Abel saw her safely in. Then he jogged to his own house. Abel wondered whether he should ask Bianca if she wanted to go to the movies or something sometime. He really had no feelings for her except that he felt sorry for her. It would probably mean a lot to her if a guy asked her out, even if it didn't mean anything.

Abel noticed that Bianca didn't have any friends at Chavez. The only guy she was sometimes seen with was Ernesto, and that was because he studied with her. Ernesto wasn't looking for a girlfriend. He was in love with Naomi Martinez, and it seemed he always would be.

So, Abel thought, maybe next week he'd ask Bianca to the movies. By no stretch of the imagination would she ever be like Claudia. But it would be nice to hang out with a chick, and it would be nice for her too. Two miserable loners hanging out together and driving away the loneliness for a little while. Abel figured that might work.

When Abel got home, it was almost midnight. He expected to meet Mom in the front room worrying about where he was. But, to Abel's surprise, the living room was empty, and angry voices were coming from the kitchen. Abel's parents were having an argument, which was very rare. It was not rare for Mom to scold Dad, but it was unusual for him to fight back.

"So why didn't you do the rock garden like the man wanted?" Liza Ruiz demanded loudly. Dad worked for Mom's relatives at their landscaping company. It was always a sore spot between Abel's parents. His father couldn't even get a lousy gardening job on his own. He had to rely on the generosity of his wife's relations.

"I asked the fool what he wanted," Dad countered. "I did the best I could. But he's a cranky old jerk, and he changed his mind in the middle of the project. I drew a sketch for him . . . the koi pond would go here . . . the little waterfall on the south side of the backyard. He agreed to everything. Then he sees the result, and he wants it all different. And I get the blame."

Abel's father was yelling. He hardly ever yelled. He was so cowed by Mom that he accepted all her scolding like a lamb. He

knew he wasn't a success in life. He knew
he owed what miserable work he did to his
wife's family. So he deferred to her in everything. He was a shell of a man whose
only feelings were shame and inadequacy.

Abel felt sorry for his father. Abel made
up his mind years ago that he would never
marry a woman who would control him
like that. Mom was a good person, and she
loved her family dearly. But she could suck
the manhood out of somebody with ease.
She did it to Abel for years, almost con-
vincing him that he was a loser. He almost
believed that his only hope for a shred of
success meant following all her instructions. Abel hated that. Dad hated it too, but
it was too late for Dad. The patterns of his
life were as firm and fixed as the cement
walls he built with his poor aching back.

"Sal, you apologize to the man and do
the job over," Mom commanded. "Jobs are
hard to come by these days. Even my family will not tolerate you making a customer
unhappy. I don't care if you have to eat dirt.

I don't care if it comes out of your pay. Losing some of your pay is better than losing your whole job. If you lose that job, what are we going to do? Answer me that. I have no other family willing to take you on just because you're my husband!" Mom's voice was shrill, even more shrill than usual. "Do you hear me, Sal? Do you understand?"

"Yeah, sure," Abel's father agreed. "I'll eat dirt. Haven't I been eating it all my life? I must like the taste of it 'cause it's all I ever eat."

Abel felt embarrassed for his father. It had been this way almost all of Abel's life. Mom treated Dad like a child who needed scolding to do the right thing and was shamed for his misdeeds. In some strange and terrible way, Sal Ruiz seemed to have begun to shrink in size. Abel remembered his father as a much taller man. Now, with his stooped shoulders, he looked shorter than Mom. Abel shuddered to think that his poor father was being whittled down to nothing. But he couldn't do anything to help him. Nobody could.

A door slammed. Abel ducked back outside. He didn't want his father to know he had heard the whole humiliating argument. When it was quiet, Abel came back inside, pretending he'd just arrived home. Mom appeared, her face flushed. "Abel! Wherever have you been? It's the middle of the night," she cried.

Abel decided to lie. "Pedro needed me to get ready for tomorrow. We were real busy, and it'll be worse tomorrow. They got a big wedding reception scheduled."

"Oh," Mom said, instantly placated. Her philosophy of life was that pleasing your employer was the highest duty of a human being. That's where the money came from. "I'm so proud of you, Abel. I think your boss must like you very much. He makes you such a big part of the planning down there."

"Yeah, Mom, Pedro really likes me," Abel replied. "The other day he said I was so good I must come from a long family tradition of chefs."

Mom laughed bitterly. "And what did you tell him? That your father is a gardener and a stone mason, and half the time he doesn't even do that right?"

Abel thought his mother was pretty. But when she was mean, like now, she looked pinched and frightening, like a witch.

"I thanked Pedro for the compliment," Abel said in a slow, pointed voice. "I told him I come from a family of hardworking people who value doing things right. I told him that last year my father built a large waterfall behind a house. It was so beautiful that strangers walking by stop to stare at it. I told Pedro that I'd never seen such a magnificent piece of stonework and I was proud of my father's work. I told Pedro that it doesn't matter what you do—a salmon dinner or a waterfall coming from a rock garden—it's all art."

Liza Ruiz pursed her lips in a strange way that wrinkled her face.

"Goodnight, Mom," Abel said, going down the hall. As he passed Penelope's bedroom, she opened the door.

"Oh, Abel!" Penelope whispered. "You shoulda been here like fifteen minutes ago. She was rippin' Dad up one side and down the other. It was so awful. Oh, Abel, I've heard her being mean to Dad before, but this was terrible." Penelope looked strange, hurt and scared—or something else, maybe terrified.

"Yeah, well," Abel mumbled.

"You don't think they'll get a divorce or something, do you, Abel?" Penelope asked her big brother. "Oh, I'd just die. Poor Dad. It just made me sick to hear them fighting. My stomach hurts. You think it'll be okay, Abel? Many times lately she looked older than fourteen. Now she looked about five.

"Don't worry, Penny," Abel assured her. "It'll be okay." Abel smiled at his sister, and she seemed comforted.

CHAPTER TEN

Cassie Ursillo was due to work when Abel returned to the Sting Ray for his shift. He'd made up his mind: He'd do everything possible to avoid confrontations with her. No matter what she said, he wouldn't get ticked off. He would just go about his business and ignore her. That was the plan.

But, to Abel's surprise, Cassie greeted him with a big smile. "Boy, Abel," she exclaimed, "Uncle Pedro is sure high on you! He gave me an earful last night when he came to dinner at our house. He said you were some kind of a wizard, and I better not mess with you. And you're not even eighteen!"

"I will be in two months," Abel stated, trying to absorb the new Cassie.

"I guess I'll just watch what you do and copy it," Cassie said.

Abel shrugged. "Well, nobody's perfect, but I've really been reading a lot of books and trying out all kinds of recipes. I think I'm getting a feel for it now."

"I bet you'll be famous someday, Abel," Cassie told him. "You'll be like those guys on TV selling millions of books and stuff. You'll be rich."

Abel couldn't get over the change in Cassie. As the evening went by, they worked harmoniously, making the special halibut and vegetables with stir-fry sauce and brown sugar.

"Wouldn't it be amazing if we ended up working as a team? The Abel and Cassie Cooking Show," Cassie giggled.

"Yeah, that'd be something," Abel murmured.

"We might even hit it off, you and me," she chirped. "I mean, I don't have a boyfriend. Do you have a girlfriend? I bet plenty of girls want to date you. You're cute and so clever. But is there somebody special?"

Abel didn't like to talk about his personal life, especially something as painful as losing Claudia. He just shrugged. "I'm too busy with my schoolwork and working here to have much of a social life."

Toward the end of the evening, Cassie came alongside Abel and felt his biceps. "My, you must work out," she commented.

"A little bit," Abel replied. "My friend, Ernie, he's really ripped. Most of the exercise I get is from lifting pots and pans."

Abel felt weird. When the girl touched him, he got goose bumps. For just a second, he thought he could maybe go for Cassie, but the idea faded quickly. He'd almost hated her at first, and now she was so nice. Abel was puzzled. He was intrigued too, but deep down in his heart he didn't think she was his kind of chick.

At Cesar Chavez High School the next day, Abel remembered his plan to ask Bianca Marquez to the movies. He thought it'd be good for him and Bianca just to hang out. When Ernie and Naomi went somewhere with Paul and Carmen, he and Bianca could go too. It was hard to hang out with your buddies and their chicks if you were flying solo.

Abel spotted Bianca walking toward history class, and he caught up to her. "You like movies, Bianca?" he asked.

"Oh yes," she answered.

"Maybe you and I could catch a movie this Friday," Abel suggested. "Then we could go get something to eat. No big deal." Abel had been very shy with girls, but being with Claudia had helped him. As much as losing Claudia hurt, she gave him something special—social skills. "What kinda movies do you like?"

"Comedies," Bianca replied. "I love comedies."

"Yeah," Abel said. "Me too. There's a good one showing at the multiscreen theater at the mall. It's got this new guy comedian who's like Jim Carrey when he first started."

A little smile trembled on the girl's lips. Abel didn't know for sure, of course. But maybe this was the first time a guy had asked her on a date, a real date. She probably hung out with guys before, in a group, but, as shy as she was, this might well be her first date.

"Thanks, Abel," Bianca said. "I mean, thanks for asking me."

"Thanks for saying yes," Abel responded. He walked to his next class feeling pretty good. He was helping Bianca Marquez out, and he was helping himself too.

When Abel, Ernesto, and Julio and their girlfriends had lunch that day, Ernesto took Abel aside where nobody could hear them. "You asked Bianca to the movies Friday, huh?" Ernesto asked.

"Yeah, I thought it'd be fun for both of us," Abel said.

"Dude, you sent that chick over the moon," Ernesto told him. "You shoulda seen her in AP History. She told me what happened, and she was so excited. She doesn't have much of a life. She's a pretty girl, but she's so shy. She went on and on about what a cool guy you are, Abel. She was so amazed that somebody like you would ask her out."

"But I'm not a cool guy, Ernie," Abel objected. "Before Claudia, I was batting zero with chicks. And when she dumped me, I was in the pits. I didn't think I'd ever crawl out."

Ernesto clapped Abel on the back and said, "You're doing great, homie."

Later, when Abel got home from school, he spotted his father working in the yard. He wasn't usually home this early. A cold chill went up Abel's spine at the thought that his father might have been fired. "Hey, Dad," Abel called out. "How's it going? The oleanders look great trimmed like that."

Dad turned. He wasn't old, but he looked old. Years ago, when he was young, he had dreams, but he dropped out of high school, married young, and quickly had a family to support. Mom steered him into her family's landscaping business.

"Yeah, the oleanders look better," Sal Ruiz agreed.

"Everything okay at work?" Abel asked nervously.

"Yeah. I apologized," the man sighed. "It wasn't my fault, but I ate dirt. Your mother called her cousin and straightened it out. Your mother said not to blame me—that I wasn't the sharpest knife in the drawer."

Abel ached with sympathy for his father. His mother shouldn't have said such a thing. Even if it were true, she shouldn't have said it.

"You do good work, Dad," Abel told his dad. "I always look at that waterfall in the rock garden on Cardinal. It's amazing." Sal Ruiz smiled a little, but Abel didn't really soothe him. All the man could think of was that he wasn't the sharpest knife in the drawer.

Abel went inside and glared at his mother. She wasn't a mean person, but she could act mean.

"Hi, Abel," Mom beamed. "Everything's okay with your father's work. I smoothed things over with my cousin. He's such a kind man, my cousin Ray. Thank God for him that he puts up with your father."

"Dad works hard for those people," Abel snapped. "And he does great work. His waterfall over on Cardinal is a work of art. They don't pay him what he's worth either."

Mom frowned. "My, you're in a cross mood. You aren't having problems in your classes, are you?" she asked.

"No, I'm doing fine," Abel asserted. "For a dumb guy, I'm really acing my senior classes. It must be a *milagro*."

Mom came closer. "I know what's bothering you. You're still missing that horrid girl who dumped you. You think you won't ever find another girl. Listen, my friend Irma Bracamonte, has a daughter who would love to—"

"Don't sweat it, Mom," he interrupted. "I'm going to the movies Friday with a real hot chick. It's all good, Mom."

"Who is she?" Mom asked.

"You don't know her," Abel responded, "but believe me, she's hot. When she walks onto campus, she turns heads."

On Friday night, Abel picked up Bianca up at the condo on Cardinal Street. Bianca looked great in a sky blue sweater and skinny jeans.

"I've never seen you looking so good, Bianca," Abel remarked. What he meant to say was that she didn't look so skinny. She looked as though she'd added a few pounds.

Bianca giggled. "I was bad," she said, holding her hand to her mouth. "I had a big cheeseburger yesterday with maybe eight hundred calories or something. I didn't even weigh myself. Not that I'm going to

193

do that often, but once in a while. Man, it was so good."

"Good for you!" Abel said.

The movie they went to had gotten rave reviews as the best comedy of the year. Both of the lead guys were excellent, and the girl was over the top hysterical. One reviewer called her a teenaged Tina Fey. The last time Abel laughed so hard, he was with Paul Morales and Ernesto. They'd gone to see a slapstick road racing movie about two dumb guys who cracked up a dozen cars or so.

Bianca was nice to be with, but she wasn't Claudia. Sometimes, when Abel was laughing real hard, he turned to make a comment, and he almost expected Claudia to be beside him. When she wasn't, of course, he felt a stab of pain.

Abel didn't know how long those feelings would last. Could the hurting time since he lost Claudia go on for the rest of the school year? But Abel was determined to ask Bianca out again. Maybe they'd never be more than friends. Or maybe eventually something would happen, and the chemistry would be right. Maybe Bianca would fill his heart the way Claudia did. He wasn't sure. But Abel did know one thing: Being with Bianca would be good for him, and it would be good for her too. Maybe that was enough for now.

The shifts at the Sting Ray had been fun. Cassie Ursillo was nice for the most part. Abel was even enjoying working with her.

When Abel Ruiz went to work on Saturday night, he noticed Cassie arriving in an old VW bug. She parked across the lot. When she got out, her thick black hair flowed around her face like satin ribbons. She was a startlingly beautiful girl.

Abel was parked nearby, but Cassie didn't see him. For some reason, Abel just stood there as Cassie looked into a mirror to check her radiant face and vibrant red lipstick. She stood under a streetlight, and she looked magical.

A man in a station wagon dropped off his son, one of the busboys at the Sting Ray. He was a nice kid and very efficient. He told Abel that he was a freshman at the community college. Cassie and the busboy struck up a conversation there in the parking lot. Abel heard what they were saying.

Cassie and the busboy seemed to know each other very well. They were chatting and laughing like old friends. In the soft night air, their voices floated toward Abel. Abel lingered at locking his car, not wanting to go into the restaurant right away because he heard his own name come up.

"Abel is pretty awesome in the kitchen, Cass," the busboy was saying. "I been working here almost a year, and I've never seen a guy so focused on cooking."

"Yeah," Cassie agreed. "He annoyed me at first because he seemed so arrogant. Like, you know, he knew everything better than anybody else. But then I realized that he really is some kind of a genius. He seems to sense just what seasoning and herbs go in every dish. It's almost scary."

"Do you like him, Cass?" the busboy asked.

"Well, he's pretty cute," Cassie admitted. "I mean, you know how I like that '50s actor—James Dean—the one who died in the auto crash? Well, Abel has eyes just like him. It's kind of amazing. And Abel is going places too. I mean, I can just see him going really far. He could have his own restaurant, then maybe a string of restaurants, like the guy who started the shrimp taco franchise."

"But do you *really* like him?" the busboy asked. "You know what I mean?"

"Well," Cassie confided, "Abel's not my type. He's sort of on the dumb side except for the cooking thing. You know there are people like that, amazing in one special thing and in everything else, not so much. But, you know, I think I could make something out of Abel. If only he had somebody to guide him along, helping

197

him through the stuff he doesn't quite understand. I mean, he must be a total idiot when it comes to financial matters. But me and my dad, we could take him under our wings. Who knows where it might lead?"

"You wanna date him?" the busboy asked, chuckling.

"Why not? He's going to the stars, and I wouldn't mind a little stardust on my shoulders too," Cassie confessed. "He might not be—" her voice was taken off by the wind.

Abel didn't hear the last part of the sentence, but he added it himself: "He might not be *the sharpest knife in the drawer*."

Abel waited until Cassie and the busboy went into the Sting Ray. Abel smiled a greeting to Cassie and the busboy when he got there, a few minutes later. They never had any idea that he had overheard them talking in the darkness outside.

Abel's thoughts turned to Bianca. He was thinking of taking her to a live show next. She'd said she'd never seen a live musical. A production of *Rent* was coming to town soon. He thought Bianca would like that. They both would.

Thinking about Bianca, Abel smiled as he got his workstation ready in the kitchen. It had been a bad time for him—a hurting time. But he had come out of it better off. His relationship with Claudia Villa had been all one-sided. He saw that clearly now. He'd just been so happy to have a pretty girl pay attention to him. He didn't really love her. He was just . . . grateful. Now he was standing on his own two feet. He could make better choices.

"Bianca's one of those better choices," he thought to himself.

And Cassie! The smile vanished from his face, replaced by a pained expression. Now he also knew why that girl rubbed him so wrong. She was so critical of him, so shallow. *Madre de Dios, ayudame*! She was just like Mom!